The Miracle of Me

A Memoir Based on
Surviving and Living With
Stevens – Johnson Syndrome/TEN

By

Alicia Bianco

The Miracle of Me
by Alicia Bianco

ISBN: 978-1-947745-21-6 (paperback)

Published by:
Well YOUniversity Publications

~ Dedication ~

To my beloved dad, for living by example, and teaching me about the power of respect, positive thinking and unconditional love. Dad, you are my Hero from the heavens and beyond. I miss you and our long talks every day.

To my mom, who emulates strength and love for her family.

To both my parents, thank you for sharing your laughter and love for life so generously.

To my children, you enlighten my soul with Joy. Bianca, Anthony and Michael I admire each of you beyond words, to say I am proud of you would be an understatement. It's an honor and a privilege to be your mom.

To the nurses, doctors and medical scientist for selflessly caring for the wellbeing of strangers; you embody heroism with grace and compassion. My journey continues due to the collective care I have received throughout my life.

10% of the proceeds from this book will be donated to aid in SJS/TEN research

~ Contents ~

Prologue
~ Spring 2013 ~

As I sat in a line of traffic, listening to talk radio, I heard a news brief – and it took no more than 30 seconds of airtime to grab my attention. "ARE YOU KIDDING ME?!," was what I said out loud to myself! Then my cell phone rang. I answered on speakerphone. It was my sister Gina, and she said, "I just heard on the radio that a lawsuit was won because it had been proven, Motrin could cause "**SJS/TEN**"

(Stevens-Johnson Syndrome / Toxic Epidermal Necrolysis is a rare, serious disorder of the skin and mucous membranes. It's usually a reaction to medication. Often, it begins with flu-like symptoms, followed by a painful red purplish rash that spreads and blisters. [mayoclinic.org])

...and this time I screamed out, "ARE YOU KIDDING ME?!" I laughed and told her that I had just heard the same thing. Later in the summer of 2013, the FDA added the same warning to Tylenol.

After more than 23 years, it had finally been confirmed. Motrin and Tylenol were two of the three over-the-counter medicines I had taken before going to see my family doctor in September of 1989. My symptoms were a sore throat, sinus headache, fever, rash on my chest and face. An old familiar surge of anxiety washed over me.

My doctor had prescribed a penicillin-based antibiotic for me after failing to notice the writing on my chart stating that I had proved to be allergic to penicillin. The combination caused a potentially deadly spontaneous combustion in my body known as **(SJS)** and **(TEN)**. What happened to me next was horrific from all perspectives and deadly for most people afflicted in the same way.

Curiosity was triggered in me, so I did a search for **Stevens-Johnson Syndrome** and came up with several websites devoted just to this disease. There was so much information available. I read about a support group for patients and family members and that August is SJS awareness month utilizing a blue ribbon as well as activities to raise money for research. I read and watched stories of survivors along with their photos. There is also a memorial page; I humbly prayed for all of them and their loved ones. None of this information was available to me in 1989. Reading and seeing photos of men, women and children who have also suffered the pain of **SJS/TEN** overwhelmed me. I've worked hard to put those tormenting memories to rest over the past 23-plus years. I sat quietly with myself while I wrote in my journal: "It's time to write my story." I continued thinking, "I can't write. I've never written (other than in my journal and a thank-you card from time to time)." I had a whole slew of low self-confidence issues welling up in my head, such as... "you're not smart enough. You don't know how to write a story. You're a terrible speller," and so on. The negative self-talk bullied fear into the thought of writing my story to post on the SJS website, so I let the idea fall away.

A few months later, a divine intervention took place, while sitting in a facilitated Wednesday night women's group. Three women sat in for a reunion night, one of whom spoke about how she started tutoring adults in writing. I felt safe in the presence of this group of supportive women. My vulnerability was still there, however, the words began to flow despite the fear that usually kept them suppressed. I said that I would like to post my story on the Stevens-Johnson Syndrome website. I briefed her on my story and the fear that has held me back from writing. Veronica is the woman who then suggested I write a few paragraphs and email them to her.

I went home that night took out my iPad Mini and began to type on its touchscreen. The memories flowed with such ease. I had intended to write a few paragraphs, and when I stopped typing I found that I had completed a few chapters! I took a deep breath and hit "Send."

Before reading Veronica's response email I prepared myself to be open to her comments and suggestions as constructive criticism. Leaning forward on my couch I read the four-paragraph letter; then I read it again. I must have been holding my breath while reading because when I was finished, I leaned back into the cushion of my couch and let out a deep breath. I felt a sense of accomplishment I had never experienced before. It was as if the little girl in my heart was jumping up and down saying, "I'm smart! I'm smart!" – much like Rudolph did in the Christmas *stop motion animated television special*, ***Rudolph the Red-Nosed***

Reindeer, when he pranced around shouting, "I'm cute! I'm cute!" after Clarice said he was cute!

Okay, she didn't actually say I was smart, but what she did write was so encouraging, it gave me hope and helped me understand that I wasn't as incompetent as I believed myself to be!

Veronica's key points to me were:
1. You have certainly underplayed your writing ability.
2. You are far past what I do.
3. The important thing is: you have a true, clear voice and a story that needs to be told, particularly to people who aren't afraid to hear it.

Wow! I had a story to tell. Veronica also offered me a great deal of options and network information regarding writing. I had heard a quote many years before: "When the student is ready, the teacher appears" – author unknown.

What a blessing I had received. After all these years of healing, God is still guiding me with love and grace.

I then retrieved my journals from our storage unit and began to read the timeline of events in my life's journey, and with each chapter I completed, another was ready to be told. I have had so much comfort, love and support from my family and friends, along with people showing up in my life to guide me in this journey of writing my memoir. It happened by a series of coincidences which make me believe that it is right on time.

My intention was just to post my story on the SJS website, however God's intentions far exceeded mine. This has been a story of blessed coincidences, and they just keep coming.

"We are confident that God is able to orchestrate everything to work toward something good and beautiful..." Romans 8:28 The Voice

Some parts of the first two chapters deal with graphic descriptions of the physical symptoms of SJS/TEN and may be difficult for some readers. If you need to skip ahead to chapter three you will still maintain the continuity of the story.

Chapter One
~ SJS/TEN ~

If raising a child takes a village, then, surviving and living with the devastation of Stevens-Johnson Syndrome /TEN takes a city of angels.

My name is Alicia, I live in New Jersey, and my story begins in the summer of 1989. I was married, and we had one child – a baby girl named Bianca Rose. My family had a party for my 26th birthday, and the big surprise was two of our cousins, Franca and Maria Pia, flew in from Venezuela. (My dad's first cousin had moved his family from Sicily to Venezuela. Franca is three years younger, and like a little sister to me. She was 14 when she spent her first summer at our home in 1979 returning each summer through 1982 – and then I went to visit her family in 1983.) So now, this was the first time her sister was visiting us in the USA, and I was so elated to see them both. We kept busy going on day trips, a concert, my brother and sister in-law's wedding, and getting ready for a birthday bash with a guest list of 70 friends and family members for our daughter's first birthday party in, September 1989.

Across the months of August and September, I had taken Tylenol, Motrin, and Contact for a headache or cramps. Little did I know, life as I knew it was about to change forever.

On Wednesday, September 7th, 1989, after returning home from work at Anthony Vincent's Hair Salon with a sinus headache, I took two Motrin and went to bed. Having had a restless night of sleep, I called my friend Karen Garland in the morning to ask if she would pick up my almost one-year-old daughter so I could get some rest. A few hours later, I was feeling progressively worse and decided to call my family doctor. The receptionist gave me an appointment for later that afternoon.

My mom had been out shopping with our cousins from Venezuela before coming to pick me up. When they arrived, my cousin Franca commented on how I looked as if I had measles. We left my house and picked up the baby from my friend's house.

By the time my mom dropped me off at the doctor's office, my eyes, face, and lips were red and swollen, and my throat was sore and scratchy. As soon as the receptionist saw what I looked like, I was brought into a private room. The nurse took my vital signs; my temperature was 102°F. They asked which over-the-counter medications I had taken. I replied, "Motrin, Contact, and Tylenol over the past few weeks." I told my doctor we were going to be having a 1st birthday party for my daughter and I was concerned for her and our guests.

I remember my doctor saying he would write me a prescription that "will take care of all your symptoms."

Knowing I needed help with the baby, my mom wanted us to stay at her house. There was a downstairs bedroom I could stay in. The guest room on the second floor had a bed and a crib for my cousins and Bianca, respectively.

I climbed into bed feeling weak; my body ached, and I felt fatigued. My mom brought my prescribed medicine to me; I took it and fell asleep.

That night, I woke up from the pain of blisters in my mouth and throat, and a biting, itchy feeling all over my body. I felt as if something had jolted my insides like I had been ignited. My mom called the doctor for me. He said sometimes you feel worse before you get better, then he called in a prescription for an antihistamine. By the next morning I was burning up with a 104.6°F fever and my back felt as if it was on fire! My mom called the office again, only to find out that my doctor had left for vacation. I asked my mom to tell the covering doctor that I was allergic to penicillin. (I had had my first reaction to penicillin after having my wisdom teeth removed in the early 1980s and it had been documented shortly thereafter.) The on-call doctor said to stop the medicine immediately! She had ordered me to take three of the antihistamines every 3 hours, get into a tepid bath to lower my fever, and call back if I wasn't feeling any better. I had already taken at least three of the pills my family doctor had prescribed before coming to realize they were a derivative of penicillin. With chattering teeth and trembling body, I sat in the tepid bath water while my cousin Franca sat on the close toilet seat across from the tub to assist me if needed. I was so weak and in so much pain. Her sister Maria Pia was helping my mom take care of Bianca.

On Friday night, my husband Bill stopped by, he came into the room and commented on how bad I looked. I asked him to stay at my parents' house with Bianca and me. I was so weak and scared. I wanted to be comforted so badly. He said his recreational softball league that he played on had a game in the morning and he didn't want to miss it. With that, he simply said, "you're in good hands" and left. I felt such disappointment. He was never one to show compassion for me, but I had hoped once he saw the pain I was in, he would have stayed.

Around 4:00 AM on Saturday, September 9th, the pain was unbearable. I felt as if I had the worst sunburn of my life, as if I was being burned alive! My eyes were swollen shut, and my mouth oozing with blisters. I went into the bathroom and started a bath hoping the cool water would help ease the pain. Using two wet cotton balls, I attempted to soothe my eyes and get them to open a little. When I went to remove the cotton balls, it felt as if I was ripping band-aids off my eyes – both sets of my natural eyelashes were attached to the damp cotton balls! With blurred vision, I was able to see a shadow of myself in the mirror. I had large elongated blisters on my neck, throat and face. I woke my parents and asked them if they would please bring me to the hospital. My parents wanted to call the ambulance when they saw me, but I begged them not to. I didn't want the commotion to disrupt my cousins' sleep. Most of all, I didn't want to frighten Bianca.

While on a gurney in the emergency room, I watched the electrodes the nurse placed on the left side of my chest peel off my body with my skin attached. I screamed in pain when she tried to put the blood pressure cuff on my blistered arm. After a few painful and failed attempts to get an IV started (due to my loss of skin and collapsing veins), the nurse used a needle intended for premature babies that finally worked.

I heard a comforting familiar voice, "Hi Alicia, its Sophia, from DePaolo's." Sophia had worked with me at DePolo's Hair Salon before I had Bianca. I had been a hair stylist since 1982 but I stopped working at that salon after Bianca was born. I started working part time at a Salon in the town we lived in when Bianca was 10 months old because it was closer to our home. Sophia was working in the hospital pharmacy and came to see me when she recognized my name while processing my medications. She asked me if there was anything she could do for me. I asked her for orange juice – I was craving Tropicana orange juice. The blisters in my mouth and throat made my mouth feel dry and hairy and I wanted to wash the feeling away so badly. It was obvious that I couldn't drink it, yet she brought it to me anyway. I felt her kindness and I took comfort in knowing she would be there for me when I felt a little better. Little did I know it would be months before I was able to drink orange juice again and would have to use a straw. It was almost a year before it didn't burn going down. To this day I savor each sip with gratitude. Tropicana orange juice with a straw is a staple in my house. I still have frequent sleepless nights due to over-the-top eye pain, so now I take two Aleve to help with the pain and Tropicana orange juice with a straw for comfort and gratitude. I also felt comfort from frequent visits from my friend Donna's sister Debby, who worked in the hospital as well.

My two older sisters, Angela and Gina arrived at the hospital after my parents told them the severity of my condition. It was my sister Angela's 30th birthday on Saturday, September 9th. When I attempted to lean in to greet them, I felt the skin on my back stuck to the sheet. It took three nurses to assist, one to support my sister Gina, as she was about to pass out, and the other two to rip the sheet from my body with the skin off my back still attached to it. The pain was beyond any other. What was happening to me was pure torture. I willed myself to stay focused on the image of my beautiful baby girl's face to push through the pain. Thank God for the mind's eye. At that time my eyes were swollen and crusted shut. I had temporarily lost my sight.

My diagnosis was **Stevens-Johnson Syndrome, and Toxic Epidermal Necrolysis (SJS / TEN)**: a potentially deadly skin and mucous membrane disorder that is usually a result of a drug allergy. I was having a DUAL reaction.

I wrote in my journal about my husband coming into the hospital with his baseball uniform on, and he told me there was talk about sending me to another hospital. He was told by the doctors though, that it would be best for me to stay where I was and that I was getting more attention here than I would in a burn unit. I said I would do whatever they told me to do. I just wanted relief from this pain.

On Saturday night, I was in an isolation room. I later wrote about how I thought I was sitting in a bus with the air blowing on me so cold. I wanted to get up and walk to the back of the bus.

When I tried to get up, I heard a voice, "Where do you think you are going, Alicia?"

To the back of the bus," I said. "It's too cold up here."

"You're not on a bus, you're in the hospital."

"Oh, okay, but I'm uncomfortable and I want to go home now." I came to realize this was more than just a bad dream.

I woke to darkness as my eyelids had been oozing with blisters, and I was unable to open my eyes. I was frightened by the thought that I had lost my eyesight. I heard voices outside my room. I was told the isolation room had large windows facing the hall, and I sensed I was on display. I was sitting up, leaning forward, keeping balanced with my hands resting between my knees on the bed to keep my skinless back protected. I had asked my nurse about the voices I was hearing coming from outside the door of my room. I heard people talking about how to prepare the family. I thought, "That poor family…," then I realized the conversations were about me!

It was now Sunday early AM, September 10th. My baby girl's first birthday was one day away. The pain in my heart was almost equal to the ripping and burning my flesh was enduring. "Please Lord, keep me alive" so my daughter will not be a motherless child, especially on her first birthday. It seemed as if I floated away from my body, and I saw the image of myself sitting naked on the bed leaning forward, and there was blood on the sheets between my legs. Yet, I felt no pain. I pictured Jesus on the cross. I thought of how he suffered with the night air biting at his torn, open flesh. "Dear Lord, you suffered pain far worse than the pain I was feeling. Thank you for your sacrifice."

I heard a male voice say, "*You will live for the Son.*"

I felt such peace, although I was confused because I wanted to stay alive for my daughter. Serenity embraced me. Then I asked about my family, "Will they be okay?"

"Yes," He said. "*They have their own.*" It was after that experience I knew I would live, and I had been heard.

My parents had gotten an update from my nurse. My condition had become increasingly more critical due to my infected, raw, and vulnerable skinless body. Thanks to a brave and educated nurse speaking out on my behalf, while putting her job security in jeopardy, she advised my parents to have me transported to a burn unit as soon as possible. In her professional opinion and experience, she believed I needed medical treatment that wasn't offered where I was. After their conversation, my parents had chosen their plan of action.

Chapter Two
~ Bladed Chariot ~

A nurse entered my room. *Did I get awaken from my dream? Or did my spirit re-enter my body?* She let me know my parents were on their way and my family doctor would be meeting up with them. This was my second day in the hospital, and I had lost over 60% of my skin. It was critical for my visitors to be still after entering my room. The slightest movement of air would sharpen the stinging, tearing pain of my naked exposed body. She reassured me all visitors would be prepped upon crossing the threshold of the door. I was told that medical students were invited to observe me through the glass. It was all so disturbing.

I missed my daughter so badly. My heart longed to hold her, and I wanted to be the first to wish her a happy birthday. I forced myself not to cry; the salt from my tears felt like acid on my raw face. It was as if my entire body had turned on me and became my enemy.

Their voices were slow and low, yet I was able to hear the conversation between my parents and my doctor. My mom asked what his plan of action was. He said something about when you see clouds it doesn't mean there will be rain; and when there is rain, it may not be a storm. My mom said sternly, in her whisper voice, "I'm not interested in a weather report. I want to know your plans for my daughter's recovery." It hurt too much to smile, so I laughed in my head. My five- foot tall mom would have needed a step stool to go head to head with my team of doctors. Without the resources needed, she went toe to toe, and demanded I be released to a burn unit immediately! I came to realize what a powerful warrior my mom is. She fought for my life and I am forever grateful to her.

It had been confirmed – I would be air-lifted to a Medical Center burn unit in Upland, Pennsylvania – about 16 miles southwest of Philadelphia. Once again, the warrior spoke out. The first helicopter that came for me was too small for my needs. My mom pointed out that I needed to be sitting up. I was burning on the inside as well as outside. Unable to swallow my own saliva because of internal sloughing of mucous membrane, I could have choked to death had she not intervened.

My bladed chariot (aka medical helicopter) arrived. Two men came into my room. I remember a kind and soothing male voice at my bedside, and I believe he introduced himself as "Joe." Still having temporary blindness, I imagined a dark-haired hero had come to rescue me. He spoke with the staff and was insistent that they give me morphine to lessen the trauma of the transportation process. I felt safe with "Joe" and trusted I was in good hands. His kindness will always remain in my heart.

After a successful, painless helicopter ride, with some bizarre hallucinations, I arrived at the Medical Center burn unit thanks to my hero, "Joe" and the pilot. My first memory was the clicking sound of the rolling gurney, my second was screaming in pain after feeling as if I was being dipped in boiling hot wax. I thought I saw a shadow of a nurse's face and then I passed out again, thank God! *{side note; my dad has a tape recording of me telling him and my mom that story on their first visit.}* When I was waking up after the first surgery (they washed me in a solution then scraped off my infected skin), I asked the nurse what day it was, and she said it was September 11th. Today is my baby's first birthday. I joked about how a year ago I thought natural childbirth was the worst pain ever... BOY, was I WRONG!

My body throbbed with searing pain; the skin under my eyes burned so badly. My nurse had placed an icepack over my eyes for some relief. I reflected on the events of a year ago: September 11, 1988... my husband had left for church at 8:45 AM. I didn't go because I wasn't able to sleep the night before. I was sitting on my couch when I felt a pop and began to feel warm water. I jumped up and ran to the bathroom – my water broke. Thanks to all the reading I had done, I knew I had meconium when I saw the color of the amniotic fluid. Within five minutes the contractions started, they came fast and furious lasting over a minute. Then 5 minutes later, another strong contraction came, and that repeated. We didn't have cell phones back then, so I wasn't sure if he was going to come home after church. I called my cousin (who lived across the street from our church) and asked if he would walk over and let him know I was ready! I had my bag packed, and I wore a maternity sundress with a towel between my legs, although by this time the amniotic fluid had stopped gushing.

My husband returned home, quickly ran into the house, gathered some things and ran out to the car leaving me in midstream of a contraction. My neighbor, Larry, having seen him run out to his car, came over to comfort me through the contractions. As it turned out, he was covering up the passenger seat to protect it from me! I thought that was unnecessary because the worst of my water breaking had already passed. My assumption was that his focus was on something other than me. To me, he seemed to be more concerned about his precious car than his laboring wife. Larry assisted me through another strong contraction and then walked me to the car. I was so angry, hurt and humiliated by what I viewed as insensitivity, I grabbed hold of his careful hard work of getting the seat protected and threw it out onto the sidewalk. Then I plopped my big pregnant butt onto the now-bare seat! A woman in labor is risky business!

We arrived at the hospital around 11:30 AM and my family was there shortly after. I wanted an epidural so badly, the pain was so intense! The nurse said I was only three centimeters dilated and it was too soon. That was around 1:50 PM. My sister Gina was with me and said she thought she saw my head spin. I was screaming so loudly, I grabbed hold of the bed rails and shook the bed like a gorilla in a cage, screaming "I have to push!!!!!!" Well, that got their attention, so the nurse came in to look at my "area" and saw I was crowning (in other words...the top of the baby's head was visible!) I went from three centimeters to crowning in 20 minutes! No time for an epidural, the baby was ready for arrival. I saw my doctor in the hall in his plaid golf pants, and he changed quickly. After four pushes, at 2:15 pm, on September 11, 1988, the most beautiful baby I had ever seen entered the world. All my pain was gone, and the love in my heart was unlike any other. Our eyes locked, and our 6-pound, 3 oz., 18-inch long baby ignited my world.

While our baby girl was being held by her daddy, I was brought into the recovery room, I could hear a bit of a scuffle in the hall. A nurse said, "I'm sorry sir but only the fathers are permitted in the recovery room." then I heard…" I am HER father and I'm going to see my daughter." I looked up and it was my dad, he kissed my forehead and thanked me for giving him a beautiful granddaughter.

I suddenly snapped out of my daydream from the stinging pain of my body and heart. I realized I was living a nightmare.

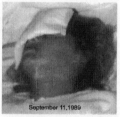
September 11,1989

September 11,1989 ~After first surgery

The surgery was a process of scraping off my dead, sloughing and infected skin down to healthy tissue and then stapling strips of a synthetic skin called "Biobrane®" to over 63% of my body. There were over 350 staples used. I was then covered in a gauze dressing for more protection. It felt so heavy on my body.

I didn't know which hurt more – my body or my saddened heart. I asked if I could talk to someone about the deep emotional loss I was feeling for not being able to see my daughter on her first birthday. A male therapist came in, and I wasn't sure if I would make any sense because of the pain medication I was on. But I later wrote what I had said to him... "I have to find peace within myself... I don't want my baby to feel my loss... I don't want my grief to be hers."

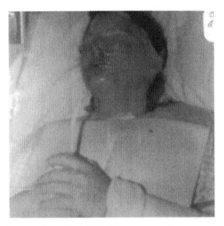

September 12, 1989 After second surgery

Sometime within those first few days, I had a dream. When I was able, I wrote about that dream in my journal. I have journaled for as long as I can remember, and I still do. *Journaling is the equivalent to prayer for me. When I'm writing I feel embraced and comforted as if I'm having a conversation with God.* While alone in the isolation room, I was reflecting on the love and heroism I saw in my mom while I was at the first hospital. We had had a strained relationship while I was growing up. Having a daughter of my own, I prayed to be the best mom I could be for her. In

24

the dream, I was sitting at a table in the presence of my maternal great-grandmother who had passed away before I was born and my Nana's sisters who had recently passed; and, there was a girl named Leah. They told me it was time to heal the women in our family from the shame that didn't belong to them. I was told a story about my Nana, who lived with us while I was growing up and who continued to live with my parents until she passed away in 1993.

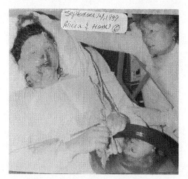

September 14,1989 ~ Alicia and mom

Unbeknownst to me at the time, that dream would have an intense life-changing effect for me and my family.

I had limited vision back after a few days. I remember I was so excited to tell my dad that I had seen a glimmer of light when the cornea specialist lifted my eyelid and examined my eyes using a powerful little flashlight. I had asked my dad to take pictures of me so I could see what I looked like once my vision returned. I'm grateful for those photos because they tell the story best and have been an asset to my emotional healing process.

I had Bianca's picture close to me while I laid in bed. I missed her so much it hurt. Upon my request, my parents brought me a large oval mirror, I hoped I would be able to see how my face looked. They also brought me a large magnifying glass with a built-in light so I could look at Bianca's picture. The first few days I wasn't able to see at all, but my vision slowly returned. In the meantime, my world looked as if I was looking through tissue paper. My dad would bring me an outfit Bianca had worn the day before on my request. I put it to my nose hoping to breathe in her scent. Sadly, the blisters in my nose engulfed the scent of dried blood; I repeated this routine daily and held her outfit close to me for comfort hoping one day the scent of her would prevail.

The only time Bianca's photo wasn't with me was when I was taken down for a dressing change each morning. The mostly male staff would unwrap or cut the gauze from my body and sponge-bathe me. As my skin grew back, the Biobrane® would lift away from my healed skin. They would use a scissor and staple remover to pull the staples out of my skin. I still have a few staple scars that remind me of the pain I had with the ones that didn't come out so easily. At first, I had a morphine drip, so I didn't mind the dressing change as much. After the morphine line was removed, it was an unpleasant experience that will never be forgotten. I experienced humility and pain on a whole new level.

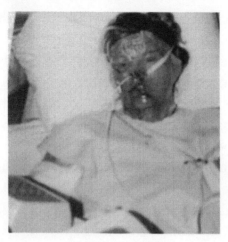

September 18, 1989

One of my night nurses was so kind – I tried to get out of my bed so I could make her a cup of tea! Once, I realized I was hooked up to monitors, lines, feeding tube, catheter, and the gross suction stick, (a tube used to suck out the saliva that I couldn't swallow, so I nicknamed it the "suction stick"!), I wanted to laugh with her, but I couldn't.

Not only was it painful, but my face had been covered in Biobrane®; it was stapled around the frame of my hairline. It felt as if I had a clear plastic bag stretched over my face, with holes cut out for my eyes, nose and mouth. I could only imagine how difficult it must have been for the hospital staff and my visitors to understand me when I spoke. I had limited facial movement from the rawness of my skin, the oozing blisters in my mouth and on my lips, and the tightness of the Biobrane® and staples. "Dear God, I truly survived a living hell."

I missed Bianca Rose so much. My dad was at my bedside every morning before starting his workday, while my mom and mother-in-law took turns caring for Bianca. I took comfort in knowing that Bianca was well cared for. My mother-in-law adored Bianca as much as my mom. My husband visited a few days a week. During his visits he complained about the long ride and how inconvenient this hospital was for him. The burn unit that would have been closer to us geographically had a nurses' strike, which is why I was air-lifted to an out-of-state hospital. My friends and family were so supportive, and I received so many beautiful gifts and cards.

One of the doctors that had come in to see me said it was time to have my IV changed again. I began to cry because my hands and veins and skin were so sensitive. Two different nurses jabbed me several times to no avail. I remember screaming and pleading for them to stop, so they called the doctor back into the room. He told me he would give me pain medication after they got the IV in. I begged him for pain meds, but I wasn't able to swallow them.

Finally, the nurse was able to get the IV-line in. The doctor stood by his word, and within minutes I had a morphine button in my hand. With my thumb on the button, that first push sent a surge of warmth while the flow of medicine entered into my veins until the pain drifted me into a comfortably numb state. It was a high that never seemed to last long enough. Still traumatized by that repetitive and painful ordeal, it took decades before I no longer had a need to talk myself out of a panic attack while having blood drawn or have to have an IV injected.

A week after I arrived at the burn unit, I still had limited vision, and my nurse thought I was wearing braces because of the thick coating of dried blood on my teeth. She wanted me to try to brush my teeth and handed me a stick reassuring me it had a soft sponge on its end. I thought, "Okay, how bad could it be? It will feel good to get the blood off my teeth." I gently put the sponge end into my mouth, but the pain was so excruciating!!!! It felt as if the stick had razors on it, not a sponge. I wanted this nightmare to end. I no longer cared about how bad my teeth looked. Vanity and Stevens-Johnson Syndrome do not peacefully coexist.

Around week #2, I started physical therapy to rebuild muscle strength. At first it was a challenge to stand on my own. My body felt so weak, all my joints and muscles throbbed with pain.

Also, during my second week in the burn unit, I was able to receive visitors. My guests had to wear sterile robes and gloves when entering the burn unit. I was overwhelmed with joy with each loving supportive visitor I had. Not only was it well over an hour ride to get to the hospital, but it had to be difficult for them to see what a bloody mess I was. My lips, mouth and eyes oozed gross pus and mucous, not to mention that my friends and family knew how badly my heart hurt. I missed my baby Bianca so much.

My cousins Franca and Maria-Pia were the first to visit other than my parents and husband. They were leaving for Venezuela the following day, making that visit so emotional for me.

September 19,1989~Alicia and Franca

Knowing how badly I looked, I asked the nurses to please prepare my visitors before they entered my room. *I looked like a cross between the movie character Freddie Krueger and the guy in the American Werewolf in London.*

Having had a bad day, I was looking forward to having my cousins' wives visit me. One of them was due with her first baby. We all have children around the same age so there was always lots of family nearby. I still feel badly about what I said to my cousin's wife, Patrice. I always felt a need to apologize for how I looked. Patrice said, in such a kind voice, "You look good, Alicia!"

I then said, "Oh, shut up Patrice!" Once I realized I said it out loud, I couldn't believe those words had come out of my mouth. It was so out of character for me to tell anyone to shut up, especially a friend just trying to be nice.

A few days later with my face still covered with the Biobrane®, my friends Mary Jane and Shannon came to visit. Shannon was a neighbor we met after moving into our condo. My husband had joined a recreation softball team with their husbands when I was pregnant with Bianca. (Shannon was Larry's wife). I will never forget the look on Mary Jane's face when she saw me on the other side of the double doors once they opened. Her face went blank and the doors had closed before she had gotten her bearings back.

On September 20th, I had a resident doctor visit me. I was due to have my IV line changed, and I did NOT want to go through that painful process again! I asked if I could try to take my medicine orally. I wanted to go home so badly, if I was able to go without the IV line it meant I was one step closer to going home. Dr. Karri agreed. Later that night, my male nurse brought my prescribed medicine, and he had to crush the larger pills. I sipped water through a straw. It was so painful, but after a few tries I was able to swallow all the pills.

Sometime in the early morning, I woke feeling as if I was burning again. I buzzed for my nurse. When he approached, I tried to open my mouth wanting to tell him how I felt. My lips tore from new oozing blisters, and blood came running down my hospital gown. He cleaned me up, took my temperature; it had gone up over 102 degrees. As I cried with pain, he brought me a small piece of wax paper with Vaseline on it put between my raw torn lips. Dr. Karin was given an update on my condition and was informed that I had said I felt as if I was burning again!

A short time later, Dr. Karri entered my room, as if on a mission to dismiss my pain. She was indifferent when she announced I was having a Post-Traumatic Stress episode and requested a psychiatrist to talk to me. I was so upset. I called my dad and told him what was happening.

My dad arrived before the hospital was open for visitors, demanding a meeting with my doctors along with the list of my medications from the hospital pharmacy immediately!

I was in so much pain I refused to go down for my dressing change and missed my physical therapy as well. Later that same day, after some oral pain medicine I had agreed to the dressing change. When the gauze was removed from my arms there were new blisters on my forearms, and in my most vulnerable private area. Oh my God! I thought, SERIOUSLY???? SJS is known to affect the mucous membrane and this was a new area of my body under attack.

I was given cold compresses to help soothe the pain between my legs. With my dad's persistence the staff discovered the oral antibiotic that Dr. Karri had prescribed for me the night before, and I swallowed, was a derivative of penicillin! It was NOT Post Traumatic Stress!

The burning feeling, new blisters and fever were yet again, a reaction to the medication. Overwhelmed with new pain, coupled with the fear of the possibility of going through the horror of the first weeks all over again, it almost took me down a dark place in my soul. My dad didn't leave my side. He comforted me through it. He talked to me about Bianca and encouraged me to move through the pain. He was my voice when I wasn't being heard. Looking back at the photos I asked him to take that day gives a visual to that trauma.

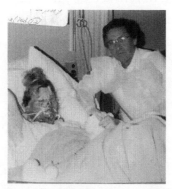

September 20,1989~Alicia and dad

September 21st was our fourth wedding anniversary. I was drained and exhausted from a high fever and the trauma of the pain that ripped through me both physically and emotionally the day before. I so yearned to be held and comforted. I hoped my husband would look past my horrible appearance and tell me he loved me. I needed comforting and compassion almost as much as I needed air to breathe that day. When he arrived, he walked to the end of my bed, and tapped my foot. That was it – that was all the comfort and intimacy he had to offer. I asked him if he would sit on the bed next to me. He said okay, but the awkwardness of his actions spoke louder than his words. He got up after a few minutes and paced around my room. I felt so broken and alone. I knew I had the love and support of my family and friends, but I needed it from him. I needed the love only a husband could provide – remembering the promise of "in sickness and in health." This was the promise he committed to, in front of God, our family and our friends four years prior to the day. The reality was, all my dreams of "happily ever after" came to a tragic end that day. It was clear to me that my heart may never recover from the rejection I felt. I knew it wouldn't help me to take pity on myself. I needed to be strong so I could get home. I hoped someday God would provide me with a loving compassionate partner – it just wasn't going to be today, and it wasn't going to be him.

I sobbed the day he told me he wasn't able to take the long ride because he was tired from being at the mall to get Bianca her first pair of walking shoes. What???!!! Is Bianca walking?! He somehow forgot to tell me our daughter had taken her first steps a few days before and was now up and running. I missed my baby's first step! Apparently, my family and friends made the decision not to tell me Bianca started walking as they thought it would upset me too much. Well, it did! I needed to go home. When my doctors told me, I would be in the hospital for at least 63 days, I thought to myself, "Oh no I won't!"

My mom called and said my cousin's wife had gone into labor. Our family members predicted she would have a boy. I was so happy for them. The baby was born on October 1st, and to everyone's surprise it was a girl, who was named 'Leah.' I smiled and said to myself, "Yep, I knew that," from the dream I had! Soon after Leah's arrival, her parents gave me the honor of being her godmother.

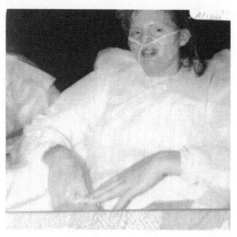

September 29,1989 ~Biobrane® lifting away from new skin

Around the end of week two, I was feeling full and nauseous; it turns out I was being overfed with the feeding tube. The nurse used an extra-large hypodermic syringe to suck the liquid food out of my stomach. She attached the hypodermic syringe to the open end of the line where the food bag hung, then pulled up the plastic syringe. The feeding tube went through my nose and into my stomach so when it was being sucked out it was nauseating, and repulsive. When they were finished, there was concern that it may have shifted and needed to be replaced. After going through that whole awful ordeal, I asked the doctor to let me try a liquid diet. I think they took pity on me and agreed. It was so painful. I had to take something called "swish & swallow." It gave my mouth and throat a light coating of protection; my mouth and lips were still so raw and oozing with blisters. I willed myself to push through the pain. It's what I needed to do to get myself home to my baby girl quicker.

My eyesight was slowly returning, thank God. I was now able to see with just a slight blur. I had to use eye drops that burned so badly the first few seconds after they hit my eye, and eye ointment that was thick yet soothing. One of the nurses wanted me to do it myself. My nails had grown so long while I was at the burn unit that it made that task challenging. She was so mean. I journaled, "I hate this nurse, she is such a witch. I could use another word, but I won't!" I chuckled when I read that! If my dad heard his girls using profanity he would say, "Such ugly words from such pretty faces." It's ironic how my values were able to hold fast back then. He never used profanity in our home. My dad is so special. His friends refer to him as "the Monsignor."

Freed from the IV pole and feeding tube, I was able to greet my visitors in the atrium instead of my room. With great will, I tolerated using the sponge toothbrush. Over time it began to feel more like steel wool – at least it no longer felt like razors. My friends and family greeted me with hugs, and it felt so good to be held. I hadn't realized how important human touch is. For me, it was as if the love and compassion from their hugs filled my spirit with healing energy.

September 31,1989~Alicia and Karen Garland

My sister Gina called and said she had a surprise visitor coming with her. I was happy yet apprehensive because of how ugly and gross I looked. I took comfort in talking to my visitors and preparing them by telling them what to expect before they saw me. As my skin healed, the Biobrane® would lift away from my skin, and my face looked as if it was decomposing. So, I wasn't comfortable with a surprise guest.

My sister wheeled me into the atrium, and there he stood... it was my high school sweetheart, Ryan. We had remained friends over the years. I was thrilled yet embarrassed of what I looked like. He lifted me from the wheelchair and held me in his arms. He told me he prayed every day for God to take my pain from me. I thanked him, then told him how sorry I was about how ugly I looked. Ryan held my face in his hands and said, "Alicia, you are so beautiful inside and out, nothing will ever change that." It was as if God spoke to me through him that day, his words replayed in my head for years. It was a healing gift for me, and I embraced it.

By day #30, I was able to use the bathroom on my own. It was a great day when that last staple was pulled out. I was able to bathe in the large stainless-steel tub. It was filled up halfway with warm water, and with assistance, I sunk into the water submerging myself into the warmth of the bath. I was even able to wash my hair and shave my own private parts, no longer having the male nurses doing it for me. I still remember the smell of soap on the washcloth. I was only 26 years old and it seemed most of the male nurses weren't much older than me. Even though they were kind and respectful, naked vulnerability was a humiliation I didn't forget.

Now that all the Biobrane® was off my body and face, I was able to see my daughter. I counted the minutes until my parents arrived in the atrium. I was now able to walk into the atrium to greet my visitors. I sat on the floor as she slowly walked toward me. I began talking to her, hoping she would recognize my voice. "Hi Dolly... come see Mommy!" "Dolly" was a nickname of endearment I had for Bianca. From the moment she was born her beautiful face was as perfect as a well-sculpted doll. When she got close enough to see me, she stopped and wouldn't come any closer. It was my biggest fear, she was afraid of my awful face. My heart broke all over again. I held back my tears and went to her. I held her in my arms and breathed her in. Her scent was the perfect combination of baby lotion, a hint of Downy fabric softener, and pure Bianca. Her scent filled my spirit. Then I began to sing...

You are my sunshine,
my only sunshine,
you make me happy,
when skies are gray,
you'll never know dear, how
much I love you, so don't take
my sunshine away.

Bianca and mommy reunite

She looked into my eyes as if she took comfort in the familiar sound of her mommy's voice, and our bond held fast. In that moment I knew it was time for me to go home.

On day #33, my husband and his dad came to visit. The nurse brought my lunch in and asked if I needed anything. I said, "no thank you," and she left the room. When I lifted the domed plate cover, I was shocked to see fried chicken and mashed potatoes. I was on a mostly liquid diet, and potato soup was the only semi- solid food I could eat. My mouth still had blisters in it and my lips were still raw. I could eat the mashed potatoes if I had some milk to water them down. I buzzed for the nurse, and when she came in, I asked her if I could please get some milk for my mashed potatoes.

She raised her voice to me and said, "I'm busy and I asked you before I left if you wanted anything."

I was hungry and so emotionally fragile after seeing Bianca the day before that I began to cry. Bill stood up for me; he raised his voice and reprimanded her for being so insensitive to me. It was the first time he had ever defended me and expressed compassion and concern. Wow! That was different! It gave me hope, perhaps something had shifted for him and he does love me.

Soon after I finished eating, my doctor walked in my room. He stood at my bedside delivering an encouraging update on the progress of my recovery. I then told him I had my first visit with my one-year old daughter, sharing I had been airlifted on her first birthday. Also explaining how emotionally painful it is for me to not be with her. I then asked him if I could be discharged from the hospital before the end of the day. I began to plead my case, saying how it would be a great opportunity for me to go home, because it might be a few days before my husband would visit again. In order for me to go home I needed a signed promissory note stating my husband would take responsibility for providing me the necessary homecare. My husband agreed to sign on my behalf. I looked up at my doctor and pleaded, "please let me be with my little girl tonight." When I saw his head nod yes, tears overtook me. I was going home, 30 days sooner than what was expected!

I called my parents first to share the good news, and then I began to pack up all my cards and gifts. On the car ride home, I cried tears of joy into a stuffed bear my cousin, Colleen, had given me. That bear comforted me through so many sad tears, and it felt good to have happy ones now. When we reached our complex, there were yellow ribbons on all the poles and trees leading to our condo. I was so blessed with my family and friends, and I was sure that God hears our prayers. He kept me alive and welcomed me home.

Chapter Three
~ Home Sweet Home ~

Like a baby's spinning mobile seeking to recover balance after one of its objects went missing, in time, with will and determination, it regains balance and begins to create a new rhythm. That best describes what re-entering my life after living through SJS/TEN was like for me.

After lining up on my kitchen counter various sizes of plastic cylinder prescription pain medicine and anti-anxiety pills for the nightmares, eye drops, eye ointments, oral rinses, oral numbing spray, and body ointments, I sat on the floor and played with my baby – just being with her exceeded any expectations I had. It was the most effective antidote.

She had grown so much in a month. I embraced the little details of her movement. I watched her little hands grasp her toys with such confidence, her beautiful face showed so much expression. The sound of her laughter was musical.

What a gift I had been given. I may never have noticed in such detail the blessing of a child at play. I made a choice that day – I chose to use this experience as a blessing.

I still grieve the pain SJS caused me and what it had taken from me. I even have a pity party from time to time, I believe that's a necessary component in the healing process. However, I set a time limit on it. At the beginning it could have lasted for weeks, days or hours. Today, I give it no more than a day, and there are times ten minutes will do.

I am gifted with a heightened sense of joy for the simple things, "simple" is not to be confused with low intellect or naiveté, but rather, an awareness of appreciating a daily task such as brushing my teeth without pain.

I know that the ONLY thing I can control is limited to CHOICE; I can only control the choices I make. I use some basic elements for balance and keep them in the forefront of my thoughts. First is to be positive and have gratitude. I choose to be happy, choose to grieve, choose to accept, choose to pray, choose to let go, or choose to ask for help if needed. My biggest challenge is letting go of other people's choices. At times, I forget that **not**-so-little tidbit of truth, which could cause me a great deal of emotional pain. Given the awareness… "They have their own" does help. In a perfect world I would remember that all the time, however, I am perfectly imperfect! I can only hope that I notice it sooner and change it faster.

Many years ago, I met a woman who was challenged with the diagnosis of Multiple Sclerosis. I heard her say, "I may have MS, but MS does not have me." I received her words, and then embraced them as a gift. Yes, I had Stevens-Johnson Syndrome, but Stevens-Johnson Syndrome does NOT have me. I inspire to pay that gift forward.

It's true that people cope with situations differently. My husband had put words to the awkwardness I sensed while I was in the hospital the day of our fourth wedding anniversary. His comments and judgments were so callous and hurtful. Reality pushed hope aside. Being criticized and shamed did not support my recovery. After my first night home I came to realize that it would be best for me to recover at my parents' home with Bianca.

There was a bitter sweetness in coming home before I regained my strength. Weighing only 98 pounds, I was too weak to lift Bianca out of her crib, and that made me feel so sad. From the moment I was told that I was with child, my soul felt complete. Loving and caring for my baby enlightened my life. Reminding myself that my body would heal helped me cope with the sadness.

All necessary doctor appointments were made. My parents were more than willing to pick up the fallen gauntlet. They provided me with all the vital necessities for my homecare. They even had a folding chair in the shower for me until I regained my strength to shower standing up.

The night terrors had started soon after I left the hospital. I would write in my journal after waking up in fear... one entry read, "It's 12:15 AM. I can't sleep, just like most nights. This is terrible, a real-life nightmare keeps coming back to me. All the pain and horrible things that happened to me in September... when I lay in bed and try to sleep, it all comes back to me as if it were happening all over again. All the PAIN, all the fear! God, I wish it would go away!" I also wrote, "People tell me how they can't believe how well I'm doing. In truth... emotionally I'm so injured, it's not as easy as I make it look. I must be strong and go on, and this is what I tell myself and everyone else every day. When my baby is asleep and I'm all alone my fears won't go away. I hate what has happened to me! I was skinned alive, and taken away from my baby, dear God make this STOP!"

My body continued to itch so badly, my eyes oozed with gooey mucus, I also had shortness of breath and horrible headaches, time and time again. I had to remind myself to choose to be grateful that I was home.

I made excuses for my husband; I would explain that he was doing his best to support me, but I withheld my definition of "his best." I was too ashamed to admit the truth to anyone, especially myself. I had so much love in my heart, I could never imagine treating anyone with such emotional cruelty. In truth, his energy felt toxic to me. I had become a master at hiding all that pain. I believed that was what a good wife and mother should do, knowing divorce wasn't a choice to be considered.

Bianca and I were surrounded with so much love and support at my parents' home. Friends and family came to visit, and my parents welcomed my guests with their kind hospitality. I hope they always know how deeply grateful I am.

First week home, Bianca, Alicia and Jessica Belsky

Having an Italian mother and grandmother made a liquid diet enjoyable – they made the best soups! Using the "swish & swallow" to coat my mouth and throat enabled me to eat soft foods as well. I wrote in my journal about how my mouth felt "hairy" when I ate, and how disappointing it was to be so hungry. Food started to smell so good yet tasted so different. Also, having horrible heartburn, I wrote, "I hate this heartburn!" My mouth and eyes were so dry and sore. I still use eye drops all day long. My eyes still tear a lot, even after more than 24 years. So, often strangers will ask me if I'm okay, because it looks as if I've been crying.

After about four months I was able to expand my food choices, but I had frequent outbreaks of mouth sores during the first few years, it lessened over time. When I'm run-down and don't give my body the proper rest, I'm still prone to outbreaks. It was a great day for me when Abreva® came on the market. Abreva® is an over-the-counter mouth sore ointment that gives me fast relief and clears up the ulcerated blisters in a few days. This is a "must have" in my medicine cabinet.

Returning to the burn unit clinic after the first week wasn't bad; they took pictures of me and recommended a cornea specialist. I went back to the clinic once a week for the first few months. I saw several different local eye doctors, pulmonary specialists and primary doctors. Most new doctors I met told me how lucky I was to have survived. Many said they only read about it in textbooks. After going to a few new doctors, I became so frustrated to realize none of them knew how to treat an SJS/TEN survivor. I only trusted my doctors at the burn unit. They understood SJS and me. I was told that one out of four survived, and that my case was so severe it was a miracle that I was THE one!

There was a possibility I could lose my eyesight. I had corneal damage and scar tissue that caused webbing around my eyes, along with scarred-over tear ducts, and damage to the mucous membranes behind my eyelids. All the damage created dry eye syndrome. My eyes are always dry and itchy. It took over a year for my eyelashes to grow back. Sadly, because of the damage behind my eyelids, I now have eyelashes that grow behind my eyelids and scratch my cornea. Eye pain is excruciating! I'm sensitive to sunlight, dust, and chemicals. Indoor pools are awful for me! Some days are worse than others. I had several eye surgeries the first few years. Even after over 24 years the pain in my eyes still torments me.

Finding the right local dermatologist was such a blessing. Dr. Terry Agel has always been so compassionate and willing to take a special interest in my recovery. He would look at my skin and reassure me I was healing well. There were days I would look in the mirror and cry, in conflict with the thought... "What if everyone sees me the way my husband sees me?" I asked my doctor if my face would ever look better. He told me I was already beautiful, and I would look 25 years old when I turned 50 due to my new skin. I had confidence in him, although I never bought the "looking 25 when I was 50 years old" theory. Perhaps it was his way of giving me hope, however, I did appreciate his effort. I always left his office feeling happy. My skin was sensitive for the first few months. I had to take frequent Aveeno oatmeal baths to help soothe my painfully itchy skin, then I would coat myself in ointments. I later used salt scrubs, then ointments. I continue to use Aveeno bath oil, cream and sunscreen. I believe that is why the scarring looks more like freckles these days.

I needed to keep my new skin shaded from sun and cold air when winter arrived. My dad brought me to his friend's hat shop. He bought me a wide-brimmed hat with a scarf attached. It did the job, but I felt ridiculous in it. I looked like a 26-year-old grandma.

By mid-November I was unable to change Bianca's diapers due to my shedding fingernails. Yep, you read it right. It was well over a two-week process. I lost all ten of my natural fingernails and toenails. They lifted off my nail beds as if they were fake nails. I would soak my fingers in a bowl of Anbesol for temporary relief of the throbbing pain, also wearing band-aids to lessen the sting of their sensitivity. It reminded me of the movie Little Shop of Horrors. If you saw the movie, the main character had band-aids on his fingers from feeding the plant. When I read my journal, I saw the pain in my handwriting. I remembered having to hold the pen between my knuckles, and there were stains on the paper from the Anbesol that dripped off my fingertips. Seeing that triggered emotional pain I didn't expect; I had to take a break from writing this book for a few days. Once again, I asked God for support and comfort.

December was here, I lost my last nail by December 17th. Yay!!! They were sensitive but no longer throbbing with pain. Christmas with Bianca was amazing, she was talking so much. My family and I had a wonderful New Year's celebration and I was so happy to start 1990. I was told most of my symptoms would be gone in a year, and I was a quarter of the way there. YAY!

January was full of new surprises. Just when I thought my body would begin to heal, it decided a sense of humor was needed. I disagreed! I had developed small pus-filled cyst on my right breast, then my left. They were sensitive at first, and as they became larger, they were more painful. I had to have both of them lanced. MORE PAIN! I also noticed my hair coming out in clumps when I combed it. I had gotten a stomach virus, and apparently going to the bathroom was so painful that I even wrote about it in my journal, asking God to make it stop. I laughed when I thought about what someone had told me years ago. "You may be able to will yourself well, but willpower won't work when you have the runs!" That is so true. My eyes felt as if they were getting

49

worse, and I learned that I had to have eye surgery. I was so frightened because I had started to lose trust in the medical profession.

Chapter Four
~ Angels ~

February was a challenging month for me, I was in such conflict with my emotions. Feeling grateful to be with Bianca was always present, yet it seemed the honeymoon phase of surviving had crashed and burned... no pun intended. I was angry ...with God, doctors, and my husband! I raged so much in my writing; I had a bitch-and-moan session with myself and God. Note... I can use the word "bitch" now without feeling guilty! It's about healing and being human.

Anger is an emotion I avoided most of my life. I prided myself in finding the good in everything and everyone. As my healing process progressed it was unavoidable – gut-wrenching purging was necessary in letting go. It seemed my anger ran deeper than healing from SJS/TEN. I began to question myself:

"Why did I marry an emotional, unavailable man who couldn't comfort me? Why did that dream I had about the women in my family keep running through my thoughts?"

My emotional circuits were on overload. In lieu of blowing a fuse, I chose to compartmentalize the thoughts that threatened my stability. I boxed up the affairs of my heart and locked them away, then chose to focus on who would be willing to answer some questions about my dream. I first told my sisters about the dream I had while in the burn unit. To reiterate, our great- maternal grandmother and our aunts who had passed were sitting around a kitchen table talking to me. There was also a girl named Leah. I was told a disturbing story in my dream, and the message I remembered receiving was, "It's time to heal the women in our family from a shame that isn't theirs." My oldest sister Gina said one of our (many) second cousins had mentioned a similar story to her years ago when they were young teenagers. I was shocked when I thought about how ironic it was that I had that dream, and how I had felt as if I had already met my goddaughter Leah before she was born.

The matriarch of that side of my family was my Aunt Jenny (Nana's oldest living sister – there were three living siblings out of nine, including my Nana at that time.) Aunt Jenny's health was fragile. After giving it some thought I remembered a story my Nana retold about my Aunt Jenny calling her up and saying, "Don't tell anyone, but the president was shot!" I laughed at that story and thought perhaps Aunt Jenny was too deep-rooted in the "don't tell family secrets" law. My next choice was Aunt Bea, my mother's cousin, and also my godmother. My mother was an only child. Aunt Bea and she were, and are still, inseparable. I thought it best to start with her.

After collaborating with my sister, I approached my godmother with care, asking her if she would confirm some information I had received. At first, she denied it. When I said I wanted to ask my Aunt Jenny about my dream she seemed to grow concerned and was insistent that I not talk to my mom, Nana, or Aunt Jenny about what she was reluctant to share.

I may have to write a sequel to my memoir to tell that story. For now, I can confirm that my Nana and my mom had overcome enormous challenges of their time. The definition of shame and surviving took on a whole new meaning for me. I began healing the depth of false beliefs that no longer had a place in my life, or the lives of generations to come.

The information I was given opened a tightly sealed bottle of secrets. With the top now loosened, it created the possibility for me to heal emotional wounds set in place over the past twenty-six years of my life due to the damage of my mother's and grandmother's childhood.

We are born without judgment; it is the negative judgment of our environment that puts "ugly" in place.

After surviving SJS/TEN and enduring years of healing, I came to realize that the shedding my skin (literally) was a metaphor for cleansing my life and healing from the inside out – body, mind and spirit. I began to embrace my life experiences as one-part burden, and three-parts blessing.

The one thing I wasn't prepared for was a medical malpractice suit. My mom had spoken to a few different lawyers on my behalf. To my surprise, one of the first lawyers said he had talked with two different doctors about my case and they both believed I had gotten SJS/TEN from an over-the-counter medication, possibly Motrin – with the probability of the penicillin derivative exacerbating my symptoms. There had never been any documentation that Motrin could cause SJS, nor was it on the warning label. With regard to the information available at that time, it did not seem feasible or probable for my mom to go up against the distributing company. She then spoke to a lawyer who said I had a medical malpractice case against my family doctor for prescribing a medication that I was allergic to. Penicillin is a known factor in the cause of SJS. There had been case studies already documented, along with the information she had received from the doctors in the emergency room. Knowing I was unable to fight for myself; this was the course of action my mother chose to pursue on my behalf. I felt overwhelmed with the thought of a lawsuit. I let my mom do what she needed to do. I prayed so much in my journaling. I asked God to comfort me, especially when I was angry.

When my nails grew back and I was strong enough to take care of Bianca on my own, I went back home to our condo. Bianca and I were home and I had tucked her into bed around 7:30 PM. Shortly after Bianca went to sleep, my mom called to let me know the hinged fold-down wall-mount table I had ordered for my little condo kitchen had come in. I was so excited that I decided to take a ride to her house so we could go and pick it up leaving Bianca home with her dad. It was the first time I drove at night since I had been home from the hospital. I had a 1985 white 4-door, Toyota Corolla. My parents lived about fifteen miles from us, so I had ample time to pick up my mom and get to the store before it closed.

I was driving northbound on the highway approaching a green traffic light. I spotted headlights of a car going too fast to stop for its red light. Relying on fast reflexes, I cut my steering wheel quickly to the left throwing my right bumper at the front of the oncoming car. When the other car hit my bumper, it caused my car to spin. I held onto my steering wheel to ride out the spin, and when my car stopped, I was facing south in the northbound lane. A woman ran up to my car as I watched the car that hit me take off. She asked me if I was okay. I must have had an angel with me – physically I was fine. But emotionally I was a little shaken up. I got out of my car and traffic was stopped by the other drivers who pulled over to help me. One of the people who stopped picked up a license plate off the road. Apparently, my bumper ripped the front license plate of the car that hit me. A gas station attendant called the police after seeing the car speed past the gas station after it had hit my car. The gas station was located on the southbound lane of the highway I was traveling on. He saw the car was being driven by a man with dark hair and glasses.

Only my bumper was damaged, so I was able to drive my car. The witness commented that they thought the other car was going to hit my passenger door. They were impressed with my split-second reflexes. The police took my information and statement, then collected statements from the witnesses. I received a phone call the next day from the police department stating they traced the license plate that was picked up off the road and found the car that hit me. My angels were working on overtime. I laughed, thinking if I were a cat, I'd be running out of lives.

I had received a summons to appear in court for a case against the driver. Sadly, after going to court there was no clear eyewitness and the driver couldn't be identified by the gas station attendant because it was dark the night of the accident. "A man with dark hair and glasses" was too vague a description to convict. The owner of the car was a woman, her insurance did pay for the damages to my car, though. I was told that her husband was already on a drunk driving "revoked" list. She said she wasn't aware her car had left the driveway that night until the police showed up. I felt badly for the officer who was on the case.

March was a better month for me physically. I was feeling stronger and I had gained a little weight back. The thought of reliving those first two months for a lawsuit against my family doctor tormented me. I did my best to put it out of my mind. I would write in my journal... "Here God, this one's for you... I want to play with my baby now."

My sister, Angela, had a bowling party for my nephew's eighth birthday in March. I had to stay in the party room to protect myself from smoke. Whenever I went into public places, I would wake up the next day with a sty in one or both my eyes, shortness of breath, and a sore scratchy throat. Back in the 1990s people were still allowed to smoke indoors. Thank God that has changed. One of the moms came to pick her son up from the party. She had on a nurse's uniform, with the logo from the first hospital I was at in September. She said she had just gotten off a double shift. I asked, "Have you heard of Stevens-Johnson Syndrome?"

She hesitated, while taking a closer look at me before she replied, "Are you Alicia?"

"Yes, I am."

She said, "I'm the nurse who spoke to your mom when you were in the ICU room."

Without hesitation I wrapped my arms around her and cried while I embraced her. "Thank you," I cried. "You were one of my angels."

Once I freed my angel nurse from our hug, she told me how close to death I was, and that she was afraid for my life. She shared that she had gotten suspended from work without pay for undermining the doctors and telling my parents they needed to get me to a burn unit. Thank God for rebels! She should have been recognized as a hero instead of being reprimanded for saving my life. Meeting her again was magical for me, and I still get chills when I think about it. She remembered that I talked about Bianca, and now I was so happy to introduce her to my little girl.

When I got home that night, I wrote about how grateful I was that God had given me the distraction I hoped for concerning a lawsuit. It was evident to me, we are never alone, and always heard.

Chapter Five
~ Bianca's Birthday ~

Sadly, my husband continued to let me know he was the victim through all this. I'll never forget the time he held his hand up to his face, as if to shield his eyes and said "Yuck, when are you going to be able to wear makeup again?" His words were hurtful, but I had so much healing to do, I refused to let his foul words define me. I saw what I looked like; I knew my face looked damaged. For God's sake, I lost my skin! But I was alive and that was all that mattered to me. Those are the times I would reflect on the gift I received that one night in the burn unit atrium. I would remind myself of what my friend Ryan had said... "God made me beautiful inside and out and nothing will change that."

In April 1990, I wrote about going to the mall with my husband and Bianca. I had seen a guy there who a friend was in the 8th grade – his name is Barry Summers. I had hoped he didn't see me because I was so ashamed of what I looked like. I felt so badly because I would have loved to talk to him and ask how life was going for him. In spite of my positive self-talk, shame won out that day. It was sad for me to re-read that in my journal 23 years later.

At times I felt weak and tired from the sleepless nights when I had nightmares. I didn't have the will or strength to get out of bed. That was when the "poor me" would kick in the front door and park it's horrid self in my space. I would forget about lunch plans or back out of play dates at the last minute.

Thank God I had an understanding community of friends and family. They have always been there for me through the good, the bad, and the ugly.

I became sick frequently because of my compromised immune system. I went back to my parents' house often that first year. Spring was approaching and my "good" days lasted longer. My definition of a "good" day consisted of fewer headaches and mouth sores, being able to eat without using the "swish & swallow," and having tolerable eye pain. I didn't want to take any more pills. I had so many prescription medications. One day I threw them all out, with the exception of the eye ointments, skin creams, numbing mouth spray and sunscreen. I had to keep my skin well protected daily.

Even though I didn't have a good marriage, I wanted Bianca to have a sibling and my husband agreed. My doctor said I had to wait at least a year before even considering it, and they weren't sure if it would even be possible for me to conceive due to all the inner scar tissue – not to mention if my body was strong enough to carry full term. There was also the concern of having a vaginal blister outbreak when it was time to deliver. If that were to occur, I was told I would have to have a Cesarean birth. No longer taking prescription pills, I was more conscious of eating healthy foods. I visualized my feet firmly planted to the earth, I freed my thoughts of doubt ... it may sound hokey pokey, but as I mentioned earlier, I knew the only thing I could control was choice. I chose to visualize my body as a healthy, welcoming environment that would nurture a new life. It gave me hope to create the possibility of having another child to love. It was empowering to keep my focus on something other than the challenges that weren't within my control.

Leah's christening was a beautiful celebration. I was honored to become her godmother. (My godparents are Leah's grandparents).

Her beauty was and still is absolutely breathtaking. It was the first opportunity I had to see my cousins, aunts, and uncles on my mom's side of the family since I had been home recovering. The last time we were all together was at my brother and sister in law's wedding on September 2, 1989, exactly one week before I had been admitted into the emergency room. It was comforting to hear how supported I was. When I look at the pictures taken at the christening, my face was reddish and sensitive, but not horrible. The camera had been kind to me that day.

Leah's Christening

After the conversation my aunt Bea and I had, I began to view my relatives differently. My siblings and I were always treated with affection – that is one of the beauties of a large extended Italian family.

I wasn't prepared for the emotions that came up for me when I learned all our cousins knew the silent story behind my dream since they were children and were told not to share it with me or my siblings. Thankfully, our generation has begun to chip away at the "don't tell all," freeing us of the shame it was built with. A few of my cousins and I began to talk openly about it, and I'm grateful for the healing effects of our conversations.

I was so excited to plan Bianca's second birthday party. This was a multitude of celebrations for me – being able to be the first to wish Bianca a happy birthday, along with celebrating my life and putting the year behind me! I could even eat almost anything I wanted as long as I didn't have any outbreaks of blisters in my mouth. Rest and minimal stress played a big part in keeping outbreaks at bay.

After Bianca would brush her little teeth, I would lay in bed with her and tell a story about …Bianca. The story was about what we did that day, and what we had to look forward to in the morning. I told her each day was a gift from God, and together we said, 'thank you' and 'goodnight' to God and our angels. Regardless of the pain and at times sadness I may have, I remain grateful for all the many blessings in my life before I go to sleep at night.

The mid-1980s through the 1990s had been a "baby boom" decade for my friends and family. My nephew was their first grandchild born in 1982 to my sister Angela and her husband Ray. They had a daughter in 1984. My sister Gina and her husband Ken had three girls, first in 1983, then another in 1985, and the third in 1987. Bianca was the youngest at that time. Within the next eight years they had five more grandchildren.

During the stay at my parents' house, my dad had a 12x12-foot playhouse built in the backyard for their six grandchildren. The noise from the hammer scared Bianca, and we would tell her that "Ricky the builder" was banging nails to build the big dollhouse. She would refer to him as "Ricky Bang-Bang" and the name stuck. We all began referring to him as "Ricky Bang-Bang." My mom decorated the window-boxes on the playhouse with flowers and hung curtains with much love and care.

While putting Bianca down for her morning nap in my parents' bed on her second birthday, I told her a story of the day to come. There was going to be a party at grandma and grandpa's house, and the party was for a special little girl who was celebrating her second birthday. I continued to tell her that her mommy was so happy to be there with her, and so many of their friends and family were coming to celebrate this special day with her. I cried happy tears while I watched her sleep, tears that no longer felt like acid burning my flesh. The memory of the pain lingered for the first few years.

I had over 100 red and white balloons, as well as lots of streamers, to decorate the yard while Bianca napped. The weather was perfect. Bianca woke from her nap shortly before our guests had arrived. Minnie Mouse was our main attraction; all the children gathered around her as she danced into the backyard. The children sang and marched along with Minnie. It was truly a magical party! I was so over-the-top happy, Bianca was so adorable, and all the children and adults enjoyed the celebration. I baked and decorated a cake in the shape of Minnie Mouse. Minnie sang and danced her way to the playhouse, then she sat in a chair on its front porch and we took pictures with each child as Minnie placed Mickey Mouse ears on top of their heads. (My friend Karen had given me wide, white ribbon with red polka dots. I made big bows with it and used them to transform "Mickey ears" into "Minnie ears" for the girls.) We had at least 25 children and over 40 adults.

September 1999

Bianca's 2nd Birthday, Bianca, Alicia and Minnie Mouse

It was my friend Donna who had rented the costume and gifted Minnie Mouse to us. Donna and I have been friends since high school, and her daughter was born a few months after Bianca. Donna transformed herself into character, and it seemed as if she channeled Minnie Mouse that day.

She put together a song soundtrack with such thought and care. Back in the early '90s there were no iPods or downloads, and a soundtrack had to be done by recording one song at a time onto a cassette tape. All her time and effort were so greatly appreciated.

When it was time for Minnie to leave, she waved goodbye, and all the children and parents cheered as she exited my parents' backyard. We all gathered around Bianca as she began to open her gifts... and suddenly, we all heard the sound of a helicopter! It was flying low, and someone in the crowd said, "Look up! Wave to Minnie! She is going back to Disneyland in that helicopter!" The children roared with excitement as they stretched their waving arms up toward the sky with such enthusiasm. It was ironic how that helicopter had appeared, as if on cue.

I remember feeling a surge of anxiety when I saw the helicopter; a feeling of fear passed through me. I knew I was safe, and I chose to honor myself by staying present in the joy of the day. Later that night I cried. That was one of the first times I understood what a "post-traumatic stress episode" felt like, while being awake. The sound of the helicopter triggered the memory of the pain. It was one year to the day. I knew I was not in any danger, yet my body responded as if the pain was real. I was learning how to keep balanced while processing all different feelings and emotions. It was a challenge for me.

There can be an average healing time on a physical wound, such as weeks or months for broken bones, but emotional healing is as individual as we are. For me, healing my emotional wounds takes faith, surrendering the fear, and reminding myself, "these feelings are NOT forever, they are just for NOW, and they WILL pass." Prayer and meditation have proven to be effective healing tools for me over the years. I had heard a metaphor for emotional healing – it's like an onion, you peel back one layer at a time. (My onion must be big!) I am so grateful for the comfort I continue to receive.

Photo of the helicopter taken at Bianca's birthday

Chapter Six
~ Blessings ~

I had my one year of healing behind me. I went to the burn unit for my one-year checkup. All was well as far as my skin was concerned. My doctor said time will tell with my eyes and lungs. I still became ill frequently with upper respiratory infections and sties when I went to public places. I hadn't had a vaginal outbreak in months, thank God. I asked if they thought I was strong enough to conceive. My doctor told me to have an OB/GYN workup then have them send all the test results. I wanted another baby so badly. For as long as I could remember I wanted four children. Knowing my husband and I were so different, I let go of that being probable and hoped for just one more healthy baby. I had so much love to share.

My tests all came back good! But as far as being able to conceive and going full term, there was no guarantee.

Bianca was all "girl." I had so much fun with her. Our neighbors Chris and Tracy had two girls, one was a year older than Bianca, and the other was six months younger. The three girls were always together. Chris did his residency at the hospital I was in before I was airlifted to the burn unit. He was one of the students who saw me while I was in the isolation room. At first it was awkward for me to know he saw my vulnerable naked, skinless body. However, I did take comfort in hearing his perspective on my condition the day he saw me in the ICU. It was amazing to hear about the odds not being in my favor, yet, here I am alive and well.

Fall had arrived, and we had so many beautiful autumn days. Taking notice of the smell in the fall air and the color of the foliage. I have always enjoyed nature and the outdoors, knowing how close I came to losing my eyesight keeps me humble. Bianca and I spent a lot of time outside with all the children in our complex. When we first bought our condo, we were all young couples, and soon after became young couples with young children.

Determined to have justice be served, my mom did all the leg work for a medical malpractice suit to be carried out. Now, all I had to do was show up for the deposition. I was frightened beyond words. The nightmares started again causing me to question if emotionally this was something I could handle. I agreed, money would help with the medical bills and no one knew what health issues I would have in the future. There were no internet searches, nor SJS support groups at that time, we didn't have home computers or internet access. Nor did my doctors have any case studies or information to offer me. So few people survived SJS before 1989, especially at the severity level with which I had survived. There was no way for me to know what health challenges to expect in the future. I didn't know I would still be living with the aftermath of this horrific disease for the rest of my life. I had no idea that it would continue to try to define my existence on a daily basis.

I didn't waste my time hoping my husband would miraculously change. With respect for my mom, I did my best and showed up for the deposition. Thinking back on it now, my daughter is almost the same age I was when I had been diagnosed with SJS/TEN. It is inconceivable for me to think what it must have been like for my mom. My mom is the strongest woman I know. I am so grateful it happened to me and not my child. My heart and prayers go out to all those parents who live the horror of seeing their child in pain.

My second Christmas was here, I had celebrated each new beginning from the day my second chance at life had begun. I love decorating for the holidays. I hadn't forgotten what my fingers felt like after losing all my nails the year before, when I struggled to decorate my condo and tree. I humbly thanked God with gratitude as the New Year approached.

I went for a follow-up with my OB/GYN in January, and I was SO excited to find out I was with child! WOW, what a blessing! Even my doctor was surprised. I chose to believe God knew my heart, and I willed my body to welcome a new life. At least it felt good to have faith that was all that mattered to me.

The joy of having another child would help me focus on keeping my body strong and healthy. As always, my friends and family were so willing to support me with any of my needs. I had to get lots of rest, as any expectant mom would. I just needed a little more than most. What a wonderful distraction from all the nightmares and pain, along with my secret sadness... a lonely marriage. I was too ashamed to admit it out loud. I had so much to be thankful for that I didn't want to seem ungrateful. I had so many blessings, so much love and joy in my heart. I wanted to be held, comforted, and desired. Instead of words of endearment, I was referred to as "damaged goods." I saw disgust and resentment in my husband's glare. Yes, I was married. Yes, he was there in body. That was how I was able to hide the pain of my loneliness from everyone – everyone except myself. I promised myself that I wouldn't live in that loneliness forever, and I knew I was deserving of love. I just wasn't ready to change it. So, I embraced this awesome blessing and enjoyed the miracle of life that grew in me.

I was raised in an Italian Catholic family. We were loving, loud, well-fed, and brought up with the fear of shame. We followed the rules and the family law... "Don't talk about your feelings, don't let anyone know what goes on behind closed doors, and always say you're fine. And, divorce was out of the question!" At least that was what I believed. In my world, shame trumped happiness. I was a good daughter and owed it to my parents to follow the family law.

My husband, Bianca and I went on a vacation road trip to the Carolinas with my cousins: Tom and his wife Patrice, their son Christopher (who is one month older than Bianca), Jimmy and his wife Laura and their baby Leah (my goddaughter who is 13 months younger than Bianca). I had such a great time with them. Soon after Patrice announced that she was expecting, my neighbor Tracy and few more of my friends were expecting as well. Once again life was full of excitement and new beginnings.

I felt great as far as my pregnancy was concerned. I had gone back to the Medical Center burn clinic for periodic exams and all was well with my skin healing. I had scars that could fade; however, I never received any promises. The doctors didn't have much to go on, and I chose not to push the subject. I was just thrilled that I was having another child.

Starting my fifth month, I thought I was past the high-risk stage of my pregnancy until I started to bleed. I rushed to my OB/GYN's office and he did an ultrasound and said I had placenta previa, which meant my placenta was low and I had to go on bed rest. My baby was fine, and the doctor said he thought I was having a baby girl. I was so relieved that our baby was okay, and I was surprised when he said "girl." I thought I was having a boy -- I craved such different foods with this pregnancy. I was so thrilled; I just wanted a healthy baby. I did whatever the doctor suggested. When I went back for my next checkup, all was well.

My high school friend Ryan and his fiancée had come over to my house soon after being engaged. When I went to her bridal shower, my belly had popped, I loved being pregnant. I greeted their moms, then I jumped when I felt arms wrapped around my baby belly from behind me. It was Ryan. He said, "Hello Bella, you look so beautiful," and he kissed my cheek. He always warmed my heart. I was so happy for him, yet my heart hurts for me. I wanted Bill to hold me that way – he never wanted to touch me or my baby belly. I went home feeling so sad that day. There was such a loss in my heart. I wanted to share my joy with my husband, but he wasn't able to receive it. I found joy with my friends and family and chose to keep the sad feelings to myself. I played the happy wife so well.

I craved roast beef subs when I was pregnant. My friend, Donna aka Minnie Mouse, visited with her daughter and brought me a sub from my favorite sub shop. Those are the memories that still make me smile. I am so blessed with such wonderful friends. Bianca had grown so quickly. She was potty-trained soon after her second birthday, and she was so vocal and playful.

I had gone into early labor at the end of my 7th month. My friend Mary Jane took me to the hospital and dropped Bianca off at my sister's house. Mary Jane was so great, she kept me laughing through my fears – the fear of the baby coming too soon as well as the fear of being in the hospital. I remember being so hungry, but Mary Jane slipped me some cream cheese and rye crackers she bought at the vending machine after I was told not to eat until the doctor came in. We giggled like schoolgirls at our rebellion. Thank God the doctors were able to stop my contractions with medicine and prescribe a daily medication that kept the contractions at bay.

I had to rest often. Still having shortness of breath, I stayed indoors as often as possible that summer. We had a pool at our complex so I would take Bianca when it first opened in the morning, then we napped in the mid-afternoon. My eyes hurt the most, and I had to get glasses early on. My eyes are still sun sensitive. I had worn glasses for distance before I had gotten sick, now I needed them all of the time. I was grateful I didn't lose my eyesight and that is still a concern I carefully watch out for. Cornea damage is a threat to SJS victims. I don't remember the dates I had eye surgery, however, the scar tissue in my eyes continued to thicken.

My skin wasn't as sensitive as it was in the beginning stages of healing, however, I had to apply sunscreen before I went outside and often while being out. I was still self-conscious about my appearance. From a distance my skin looked okay; it was close up that bothered me the most. I had taken Bianca for an eye exam when she was young. I always told my children's doctors they couldn't have penicillin because I couldn't give it to them – both because I can't touch it, and also because I'm not sure if they have allergies to it, like me. When I told her pediatric eye doctor it was because I had SJS, his reply was, "I just thought you had bad acne." That insulted me so much. I knew I looked bad, I was still self-conscious, and that comment hit a female nerve. I only had pigment damage and some raised scars. Burn victims have so many more challenges than I have. I still feel a level of guilt when I think about how lucky I am.

I had been in the hospital twice for early labor. Now that the baby was big enough and they believed her lungs were developed, I was taken off the medication. Ryan's wedding was approaching. I called his fiancée and apologized for the last-minute regret, but I didn't want to risk going into labor at their wedding and with my sketchy hormones all over the place I didn't want to have any buried emotions escaping from their padlocked cell.

Chapter Seven
~ Birthday Gift ~

I had taken Bianca to pick peaches with our neighbor at a local farm and I was craving peach cobbler. I had prepared to make it in the morning. Bianca and I went outside to play early the next morning. Tracy and the girls were already outside, and Chris was also home that morning. Tracy's due date was only a week after mine, and to me she barely looked pregnant. By 9:00 AM I felt as if I started to have contractions. I called my husband to let him know, then I called my friend Mary Jane to ask if she would be able to give me a ride to the doctor's office if the contractions continued. There was no making peach cobbler that day. My contractions built a strong pattern quickly.

Mary Jane brought Bianca and me to my sister Angela's house. My sister lived one mile from my doctor, so I labored at her house until my contractions were three minutes apart. When I walked into my doctor's office there was a waiting room full of women. I thought, they're not going to be happy with me if they all have to reschedule, and they did. I had my doctor promise I could have an epidural as soon as I was checked into the hospital and he agreed. When Mary Jane and I walked out of his office I held onto the railing of a ramp for balance through an intense contraction. My husband pulled up to the opposite side of the railing, put the passenger window down, leaned over the seat and yelled out to me... "Alicia! Stop making a scene!"

Before I could react, Mary Jane yelled more profanities than I had ever heard, using his name before and after each one. I was laughing and crying all at the same time. I wanted her to be my delivery coach, not him.

I got my epidural as my doctor promised. Soon after I was ready to push, it was a beautiful and painless birthing experience. When the doctor held up my baby, the first thing I said was, "What's that between my daughter's legs?" He laughed and said, "Your son!" I knew it! I knew I was carrying a boy!

He was so beautiful. I must admit, we make beautiful babies. Anthony Joseph was arrived weighing in at 6 lbs., 3 oz., and 20 inches long. He arrived the day before my 28th birthday – what a wonderful birthday gift I had received.

My husband was happy to have a son, and he brought Bianca to the hospital to meet her new baby brother. We looked like the ideal little family. Our friends and family had arrived as well, and I was a little shaky from the epidural, but other than that, I felt great. I had the "new baby high"!

Being at the same hospital that I was in when I had SJS was a little unnerving. I did what I learned to do so well and put those feelings away.

The hospital offered a "surf and turf" dinner to the parents the day after delivering, and it was also my birthday, so I was excited to go. My husband had come to see us early that morning and was star-struck by the newest member of his favorite band sharing our room. They had their baby early in the morning, and it turned out that a member of that band was married to the sister of a guy I grew up with, so it was like a reunion for me. They had a big family, and it was nice to see them all.

I wasn't surprised when my husband didn't show up for dinner, he had some excuse and I guess I blocked it out. (Reading that in my journal made me feel sad) The hospital did have a cake brought up to my room that afternoon, and it was fun because Bianca was there when they brought it.

I loved being a mom, it all came so easy for me. I was a little too confident while I was delivering Anthony, the epidural was numbing so I didn't feel the pain until I got home. Sitz baths are the best! Nursing was a bit of a challenge the first few weeks as my skin was sensitive, but I stuck with it and was able to nurse him for one year. It took a few weeks for my body to regain strength. Considering all I had been through just two years before, I was so grateful for how well I felt.

I had my class reunion three weeks after Anthony was born. I had talked Ryan and his new wife into going, so I couldn't back out. I wore a lot of makeup that helped cover up my scars. I only gained 20 pounds with this pregnancy and lost 25 pounds, in two weeks, so I knew I looked thin with big breasts. I loved that! I felt good in my short skirt and fitted top, until I started talking about my children with my classmates. The power of suggestion takes on a life of its own when you're a nursing mom. It took all of a few minutes for my breast milk to leak through my breast pads and added two large wet circles to my lovely fitted top, framing my new large breasts. I went into the lady's room attempting to dry out the rings by awkwardly positioning myself under the wall hand dryer. Well, that was an epic fail, it just set the stains in deeper. I now know dried breast milk stains clothing. Needless to say, my night was cut short. The greatest part of that night was feeling good about the way I looked. My husband had even given me a compliment.

My face reacted to the makeup the same way Cinderella's dress reacted to the stroke of midnight. It went from nice to nasty – I had broken out so badly. It was the first time my face hurt since I had been home from the burn unit. I definitely wasn't going to wear that much makeup again any time soon.

My two children brought so much love and healing to my spirit. I began to feel pure joy in my heart. I enjoyed life again. My pity parties were few and far between. Even the nightmares stopped tormenting me, with gratitude to God and my angels. It was safe to say the worst physical symptoms caused by Stevens-Johnson Syndrome, other than my eyes, had passed. I took comfort in knowing I had the faith and strength I needed to overcome whatever would lie ahead.

Chapter Eight
~ Precious Moments ~

With each new season of my life there were joys and unavoidable challenges. Both mine and my husband's grandmas had become ill. My Nana Millie developed emphysema after years of smoking, and his Nana Celia was diagnosed with dementia. I would take Bianca and Anthony to visit his grandma and grandpa most Wednesdays for lunch; they were the sweetest people. She served Ramen Noodles and an assortment of lunch meats. I loved his family from the first time I met them, which was our second date. There was an instant connection. We were both third generation Italian descendants, culture and tradition ran deep in both our families. His family welcomed me as if I was one of their own. I had wondered if it was because he hadn't dated much and were thrilled that he found someone. I also spent a lot of time at my parents' house to help my mom with Nana – she was on oxygen and eventually a home IV.

It was a joy to see how the great-grandparents would light up when the children were with them. It's as if great-grandchildren are God's elixir for the elderly. We always left Nana Celia's house with a trinket from her collection of china.

My Nana always gave the children a dollar. The spirit of our children had such a positive effect on our grandparents. Those are such precious memories for me.

Anthony's christening was in the Fall. My sister Gina and my husband's brother stood up as godparents for him. We had a beautiful party to celebrate the event at a restaurant near my parents' house. His family drove in from out of state. I love watching the videos that were taken that day, seeing and hearing the voices of the family members who have passed keep their memories alive. I was so fond of his uncle; he was such a kind and loving family man much like my brother-in-law. I had admired the affection both men had for their wives, and their natural ability to embrace their children. They both adored Bianca and Anthony, I had hoped my husband would someday reflect the actions of his brother and uncle by showing me and our children the same love and warmth I saw in them.

My husband had three younger, almost-adult cousins, and a brother that had four children. We were such a big crowd, there was always so much family to enjoy.

The pain in my eyes caused frequent visits to the eye doctor, and I needed another eye surgery. It seemed as if the stress from the pain had settled in my neck, and I developed such a stiff and aching neck. My sister Gina gave the best massages. Some days I would go to her house with the children just to have her rub my neck.

While I was nursing, it was vital that I had the proper nutrients. I began to get mouth sores again and eating became so painful that I started losing weight. I had to start drinking Ensure again. I hated the taste so much, and it brought back so many bad memories. It's amazing how my taste buds could trigger a body memory. It was like all my senses become heightened, even the smell of the liquid bath soap I was sent home with triggered memories of going down for my dressing change. At that time there wasn't a medication that lessened the healing time of mouth sores. I used whatever the doctors had to offer.

I was only overweight one time in my life – it was after I started working full time in a hair salon back in 1982. There were always bagels and pastries around. The staff would send out for hot dogs and fried foods for lunch and dinner. After about a year of eating that way I realized leggings and oversized shirts had become the only clothing in my wardrobe that fit me! I went from 115 pounds to 140 pounds, and I was mortified! I joined a gym and changed my relationship with food. It took about six months before I was able to fit into my jeans. I vowed never to do that to myself again. When I was pregnant with Bianca, I read the book, *What to Eat When You're Expecting*, and that became a nutritional bible for me. I gained 17 pounds with the pregnancy and lost 22 afterward; I always recommend it to expecting moms.

While nursing Anthony I did all, I could do to keep weight on. I was told while my skin was growing back it burned out fat cells in my body. The most noticeable feature that changed is my face. Aside from the texture of my skin, my face had been much fuller. I looked as if my entire body structure had become smaller, which I guess it did. I am more petite than I had been before I had gotten SJS. It's nice to be thin, however, I most definitely wouldn't recommend SJS as a weight loss option!

Bianca's third birthday theme was horses, and my brother-in-law Ray baked and decorated two rocking horse cakes. We had a pony brought over to my parents' house, and each of the children received a cowboy hat when they rode the pony. Once again, I had a blast with all the preparations, and the party was a great success!

My baby girl had become a little girl in a blink of an eye. The day I took her to orientation at a Nursery School, I was talking to one of the moms who had asked me if I were okay; she thought I had been crying. I explained my eyes where tearing as a result of an allergic reaction called Stevens-Johnson Syndrome. She then realized I had been her patient of hers before I was airlifted to the burn unit. We were both happy to share our stories with each other.

Bianca had long dark hair – with her big brown eyes she looked like a little Italian princess to me. Halloween was so much fun. My sister gave her a bride costume and she wore a veil and carried a bouquet of flowers. I showed up at her preschool to take pictures with Anthony. He wore a one-piece tuxedo and I glued a plastic mustache to his pacifier and pinned a flower on the lapel. They looked so adorable, dressed as a bride and groomsman. I had so much fun with my children. It was a blessing that I didn't have to go back to work, not that I could even if I wanted to. I wasn't able to work in the salon due to all my residual health challenges.

My lungs and eyes were still sensitive, and the fumes generated in the salon would have been toxic for me.

There were a series of depositions I had to go through. Talking about what I went through in detail jump-started my nightmares. They were haunting. There were times I would stay awake and wait for Anthony to wake up so I could embrace the joy of nursing him. This always knocked those fears out of my head. He was so beautiful. My sweet little boy brought me so much joy. Nighttime with him was such a gift, quiet "mommy and Anthony" time coupled with the blessing of distraction.

Our condo had two bedrooms. Using my creative talents, I set the children's bedroom up as two rooms. Bianca had a loft bed, and her side of the room had a rose chair rail border. There was a little kitchen set up in the opposite corner. Under her loft bed was a vanity, and a lace valance hung at its entrance. When Anthony became mobile, we had to gate off Bianca's side to protect it from his wrath of destruction. Anthony's side was all sports. My parents bought a 4-foot hand-painted floor lamp, made to look like three children dressed in all three of my husband's favorite sport teams – a Giants football player with a football tucked under his arm, a Mets baseball player holding a bat, and on the bottom was a Rangers hockey player with a stick and puck. The lamp was a baby shower gift when I was expecting Bianca because my family assumed, I was having a boy! At that time, I didn't want to know the sex of the baby when I was pregnant. I carried all in the front, so they believed that meant it was a boy. So much for those old wives' tales! It was such a cute setup. Bianca loved playing house with her baby brother. My six-year-old niece, Angela, spent a lot of time with us. She was like a little "mother's helper." They had tea parties and made forts using sheets and blankets. I have so many priceless memories with my children.

Chapter Nine
~ Knowledge is Power ~

The summer of 1992 came quickly, and Anthony was getting so big. The anticipation of him taking his first steps was exciting for me. It seemed with each new milestone I had an underlying feeling of fear that had to be fought off. The fear of missing his first birthday, missing his first steps… I'm not sure if there is a clinical name for what I was experiencing. I don't think it was Post Traumatic Stress Syndrome – maybe it was a normal part of healing, or was it the unmentionable… "God forbid," as my mom would say, "depression." That word seemed like the ultimate curse word from what I had been told. I had never thought about going to a grief or support group, nor do I recall it being offered by any of my doctors. I did see a therapist a few times, but it didn't seem to help me. My friends were great, yet, I didn't have anyone who could identify with what I was going through. I had such grief over what I had lost, coupled with guilt for wanting to grieve. It was all so overwhelming. There was also some old deep-rooted message that played in my head…" Therapy is for the weak-minded." That stunk! "Now I'm weak-minded too?!" I had become a master at hiding my pain, there was so much sadness and loss built up in me.

I knew what I wanted was not an option.
I'm just living a lie, acting out the role of happy housewife - compartmentalizing many different feelings and emotions, three of which I wrote about the most:

First: The purest blessing of my life is being a mom. My children are the foundation of truth in my spirit. I know they have been gifted to me; I hope they know how special they are to me. "May they grow in good health while living the awesome life intended for them." I enjoyed all the details of motherhood; I would sit on my floor and play with my children for hours. I love planning and having parties too.

Second: The life of illusion – I knew I was marrying a man who was incapable of loving me in a way my heart desired. He was the perfect fit for my family, and I was the perfect fit for his. It was clear to me that he wasn't emotionally available, yet he had so many other qualities I thought was needed for a good marriage.

My high school friend Ryan and I started dating in our junior year of high school. We grew into young adults together, planning our future with the freedom to dream about our "happily ever after." His dad passed away when he was only four, and my parents welcomed him into our family as his welcomed me into theirs.

By the time I was 21, I wanted out of my house so badly. The mother-daughter dynamic was unbearable. Both my sisters had gotten married in their early twenties, and my mom and Nana were like oil and water.

My dad and I would go for long walks when the tension became too overwhelming, and he would tell me my mom doesn't realize what she says when she is upset. I called those walks "guilt walks." My mother came up with the nickname for me..."mother hater." It seemed she was jealous of my relationship with my dad. My mom spent her time with my two older sisters when I was young, however, I did enjoy spending time with my brother and my dad. I had been shamed into believing "good girls" live with their parents until they're married. I was on a mission to save as much money as I could, then get married as soon as possible. My plan was going well, and Ryan seemed to be on board, except he didn't have the same urgency. He wasn't ready to stop partying and hanging out with a crowd that didn't share my values. I knew he loved me, and I loved him as well, however my need to move out was one of urgency. Our relationship ended with a painful breakup.

By 1983 I had saved enough money to buy a two-bedroom condominium in the same town my parents lived. The pre-construction price was $68,000 with a fireplace. I had a substantial down payment saved, even after I put a deposit that was being held. I had only worked full time for one year at the salon, so to qualify for a mortgage I needed a co-signer.

I told my dad about the five-year plan I had in place, covering my monthly expenses with one paycheck out of four, and I would be renting the second bedroom to a girl I knew from work, and I would apply the rent money toward my savings. My dad and I discussed it further, before he finally agreed to be a cosigner on the mortgage. He wasn't an easy sell at first, however, he was supportive of our final agreement. Now it was time to present my exit plan to my mom. After approaching my mom, there was no discussion to be had...my mom went postal on me, yelling that her "girls don't move out until they are married"! She continued yelling that I would be the shame of her family and went on calling me such awful degrading names. I had hoped my dad would have defended my honor; I so badly needed him to stand up to my mom on my behalf. His way of intervening entailed driving me to retrieve the deposit check at the sales office, and then driving four hours to our Upstate NY vacation home where I spent three days crying while my dad cut the grass. I was crushed on so many levels; I remember feeling such severe stomach pain, in a word, I felt **broken**. I had lost all hope of moving out before marriage.

I met a guy soon after. He had just moved into an apartment with a co-worker after his parents informed him that they sold their family home and purchased a house in a retirement community. He was told that 26-year-old men should do the "right thing" and find a wife. He seemed to be in the market for a wife and I wanted to move out of my family home.

Around 9 months after my breakup with Ryan, he and I reconnected. I had only been dating this new guy for three months when we became engaged. It broke my heart when I saw the pain in Ryan's face after I told him I was engaged. We vowed to remain friends and will always be in each other's lives. What I hadn't realized was that our friendship filled the emotional void I had while I was married.

I can't blame my husband for who he is; he held up his end of what our marriage was based on. He was responsible, while financially supporting me and our children. He loves our children and I know he steps out of his comfort zone to his best ability for them. However, the emotional partner I longed for moved on and had his own life. This was all on me. The consequences of my choices ripped through me.

There were many layers of that onion metaphor, and it took the healing from SJS to peel them away. I think I know why an onion is used as a metaphor – it stinks and makes you cry.

Now what? I prayed for guidance, I prayed for answers. My personal lesson became, "Be careful what you pray for!"

Third: Living with the devastation of SJS. I had lived through physical and emotional torture. I continue to have daily eye pain, every day! No living being should have to withstand the pain and devastation of SJS/TEN. There is no sugar coating it – it's a lifetime healing process.

My hope is that all those in the medical field become better educated in the cause and effect of this devastating reaction. "Knowledge is power." Being able to identify the symptoms as soon as possible gives the medical professionals the POWER to lessen its effects sooner. How does one's body turn on them so violently? Why does this happen and what caused my symptoms when I woke up that Thursday morning before going to my family doctor? Why did I feel such a shift of inner pain after taking the antibiotic? I know I didn't live through the horror of SJS/TEN in vain. I did my best to keep balance. Act as if all is well, staying present in every day is what I choose to do.

My husband and I rented a house for a week at the Jersey shore. It was next to my friend Mary Jane's house. We had different houseguests each day. I love entertaining. I only spent an hour in the early morning on the beach to keep my skin protected. At that time my skin was only three years old. Nighttime was my beach time... I loved sitting by the ocean and listening to the waves crashing on the rocks, then hearing the water being pulled back into the ocean. I would imagine it as a cleansing for my life... God washing over me and taking away all my pain while offering me a new beginning. I found refuge from my emotional pain whenever possible, nature offers an unlimited amount. Utilizing it helps me to keep my mobile of life balanced.

Anthony's first birthday party was celebrated at my parents' house with my nieces and nephew and a few close friends and relatives. The theme of his party was Big Bird and Cookie Monster. My little man was so cute – he had just started walking at that time. I baked his theme cake and had party games planned for the children. My day was gratefully full of love and joy. I was finally able to put my fear of missing his "first birthday" to rest.

Ryan's wife called me and asked if I could lend her my maternity clothes as they were expecting their first child. I retrieved my box of clothing and went to drop them off to her a few days later. Ryan was home sick the day I went there, and I was disappointed when he didn't come out of their bedroom to greet me. I was secretly looking forward to seeing him.

Fall was here and we had another fun Halloween. I love holidays and I decorated Anthony's stroller with green and brown fabric, then attached felt pumpkin leaf cutouts to it. He wore a pumpkin costume – he was a pumpkin in a pumpkin patch. Bianca was dressed as a red crayon that year. She was so adorable.

My friends and I had gotten together for a "Girls Night Out" to celebrate all our birthdays. I have never been one to drink liquor, so I would definitely be in the category of an "inexpensive date." Mary Jane was my designated driver. I didn't leave the house until Bianca and Anthony had fallen asleep; their dad stayed home with them. We danced all night. I had so many different men asking me to dance, I thought my friends had something to do with all the attention I was getting. It was a well-needed confidence builder. I don't remember when we arrived home. I quickly learned, children and hangovers are a force to be avoided!

As I had mentioned earlier, people were still allowed to smoke in public venues that caused havoc on my health. While recovering from "Girls Night Out," I woke up with sties in both eyes and an upper respiratory infection. I was sick for weeks afterwards.

I wrote about what a challenge my health issues must have been for my husband. He and I never shared our feelings with each other. I had no idea how he was coping with life after SJS.

Chapter Ten
~ The Bassinet ~

It had taken me longer than usual to recover after my Girls Night Out. Residual scar tissue in my lungs and esophagus prolonged my healing process. I was told after having a bronchoscopy that I have the lungs of an 80-year-old smoker. I'm still sensitive to cigarette smoke. Thankfully few of my friends still smoke. I do my best to stay away from it, however there are times it's unavoidable, such as walking into or out of a mall, store, or restaurant. In only a few moments of being around it, my throat feels sore and scratchy and my lungs get a heavy feeling. The scratchiness of my throat causes my voice to sound hoarse. Over the years, I have used many different inhalers for temporary relief.

I do my best to be compliant to the elements that will cause me pain and illness. There are times I choose to accept the consequences by rebelling against what's best for me. I will go to a fair, visit the city, walk on the boardwalk and so on. I know it will cost me some recovery time; I refuse to back down. I push myself when there is something that is important to me. SJS pushes me back, however, I put up a good fight.

The lawsuit was moving along, and I was sent to various doctors, some for our case and others for the defense. The nightmares were back and so were the headaches along with an awful stiff neck. I had even gone to a chiropractor with the hope of getting some relief.

Anthony was able to tear into his own Christmas presents in 1992. Bianca was four years old already. Holidays with my children are quintessential. Regardless of my physical and emotional challenges, their beautiful spirits bring me so much joy.

After the holidays I was feeling fatigue again, more than usual. Anthony was an active toddler, so I thought that may have had something to do with it. I had gone to my doctor for a checkup and was pleasantly surprised to find out I was expecting again. WOW! Another blessing! My biggest concern was keeping my body strong enough to carry a full-term pregnancy. I was having more outbreaks of blisters in my mouth which made eating painful again, coupled with feeling physically fragile weighing a little over 100 pounds.

I would pray with my hands resting on my baby belly ...doing my best to keep my baby and my body strong. With my eyes closed, I could feel a presence of peace and comfort knowing I wasn't alone.

I collected my maternity clothes from Ryan's wife and lent them our family bassinet. It had been used by all seven of my parents' grandchildren, and now Ryan's son would be using it as well.

Bill was working the day of their son's christening, so I brought Bianca, Anthony and my baby belly. Ryan had a large family also. His sister and I were friends and we spent time together with our children. Bianca had a lot of fun with all the children her age. Anthony wanted to join in the activities, so I tied a red helium balloon to the belt loop of his pants to help me keep track of his socializing. Toward the end of the party I had lost sight of the red balloon and I began to panic. I looked outside first; thank goodness he wasn't out there. Just as the cake was ready to be cut the table began to move... and out popped the red balloon! I felt a sense of relief, coupled with embarrassment. He quickly became the center of attention.

We received a call from my father-in-law, his only brother had gone into the hospital for a hernia operation and he wasn't doing well. We had been to Long Island just a few weeks before, and now he was home recovering after the surgery in more pain than the doctors had prepared him for. He then went back into the hospital and at the young age of 50, passed away from a surgery gone wrong, leaving a wife and three teenage sons. It was so tragically sad.

There was a terrible snowstorm; we had such a hard time trying to get to Long Island. It had taken us several hours to get there. The normal travel time would have been under three hours. Uncle Gene was one of my favorite people. He was the most amazing husband and father as well as a beautiful, kind-hearted man. His occupation was New York City fireman. Firefighters are the most selfless heroes; he was a wonderful cook as well. His passing seemed so senseless. I guess God needed him. He is still greatly missed.

That spring, while at the playground with the children, I met new neighbors. Their condo was next to the pool.

Symantha and Scott had three-year-old twin boys. Sym was a nurse and we became friendly soon after meeting. She had recommended putting Tums on the ulcers in my mouth for some relief of their stinging pain. It did seem to help a bit, nevertheless, I had to go back to drinking Ensure. It was more of the memory around that drink that bothered me, not its unpleasant taste.

Sometime early that spring, I invited Symantha with her twin boys to my parents' house for lunch. My parents live by a lake, and with the playhouse in their yard it was always a fun place for the children. My Nana was ill and on home oxygen. She stayed in my parents' family room during the day, the family room was off an enclosed back deck separated by sliding doors. Symantha's boys had a great deal of energy back then. My Nana was known as one to speak her mind, and after her illness progressed, she seemed to lose her opinion filter. The boys were making my Nana crazy, and I heard her call out to Symantha, "Hey Symantha, how do you manage to keep that fat ass while running after those two boys?" I couldn't help laughing when Symantha came back with, "Careful, Nana, or I'll close that oxygen hose in the sliding door." I was embarrassed yet entertained by their sarcasm. (Symantha was a nurse, so she knew how to handle herself with the elderly and did it with such ease! Not to mention, Symantha's shape was the future envy of a woman's body.)

Laughter is one of the best elixirs to healing. One of my friends whom I met in high school is like a healing guru when it comes to laughter. She is gifted with the ability to transform all her challenges into a one-woman comedy show. Her witty sense of humor supported me with gut-wrenching, almost "pee your pants" laughter when I needed it most. Within minutes of our phone conversation, I could go from being in my pity pot to laughing hysterically. Those countless conversations were so healing.

By year four of healing, my life had begun to shift. Carrying my third child was a blessing beyond my expectations. Sadly, we had so much loss that year. We lost three of our grandparents, along with Uncle Gene. It was such a sad time for all of us.

All was going well. Bianca and Anthony were invited for playdates on the days I needed rest the most.

The children and I went to our favorite "U-Pick" farm with our friends to pick strawberries. It was the same farm we were the day before Anthony was born. We joked about picking fruit had brought on my labor with Anthony. That night, after putting my two exhausted children to bed I began to iron. Symantha called, and when I told her I was ironing she laughed and said: "you must be in the nesting stage" because she knew I didn't like to iron. Around 9:00 PM I felt a contraction, then ten minutes later another. I told my husband that I may be in labor, however, he believed it to be false labor. I called my doctor around 10:00 PM because the contractions were more consistent. I wasn't due for another four weeks, so I hoped if it was early labor the doctor would be able to stop it as they did when I was pregnant with Anthony. My husband became indifferent after I told him we had to pack up the children and bring them to my parents' house. He said he had work in the morning and didn't want to waste his night in the hospital.

Him: "You're not in labor, Alicia, it's all in your head!" he said.

Me: "I've had two children already; I know what labor feels like!" I retorted.

I couldn't believe he wouldn't take me to the hospital, so I called my parents to let them know that I was going to drop the children off and take myself to the hospital. My dad became so upset, he had me hand the phone to my husband. After their conversation he angrily got up and stomped around the condo to get himself ready to leave. I packed for me and the children ... and off to grandparents' house we go!

Chapter Eleven
~ Grace ~

By the time we arrived in the emergency room it was after 1:00 AM, and I was quickly sent up to labor and delivery. I began to dilate, and it was now too late for the doctors to stop my contractions. I was so scared, I was going to give birth four weeks early. My dad encouraged me to keep positive upon leaving my parents' house. I needed to stay focused on bringing my baby into this world with peace and serenity.

My room looked like a fancy hotel room. It was a brand-new wing of the hospital, completed just three days prior. We were the first delivery in this gorgeous room. There was a chaise lounge and large TV with the remote control and a large beautiful bathroom to the left side of my bed and French doors to the right. The full view window was encased with a pillowed window seat that could be coupled as a twin-size bed. The walls were painted in soft pastels with lovely prints that hung in frames. I walked around the room taking videos while my husband watched TV.

Before getting my epidural, I let the nurses and doctors know about all my allergies and informed them about my sensitivity to getting an IV. I briefed them on what SJS is and why I am so sensitive when getting an IV. My nurses were always compassionate and understanding to my needs after my explanation.

It was great to watch the contraction monitor hit high levels and only feel a little pressure without being in pain, after the epidural was started. My only complaint was the cold air blowing from the vent over my bed. I still don't like cold air blowing near my face, it reminds me of the pain I had when I had lost the skin under my eyes, and those memories still have a tendency to get triggered.

We were able to rest for a few hours while I continued to dilate. By 10:30 AM I was at 9 centimeters. A team of nurses came in and opened the set of French doors, and out came all the equipment needed for the birthing process. It was all so fascinating to me. I didn't have any of this high technology and luxury with Bianca or Anthony.

My husband stood to the top left side of my bed with the video camera and taped our third child as he breathed his first breath of air. The doctor placed our beautiful six-pound, 21-inch baby boy on my chest. His face was angelic. Michael, the archangel, was the first thought I had when I saw my beautiful boy. There was no doubt about what to name him, Michael Gene. The nurses cleaned him up and then handed him back to me. He had gotten a 9.9 appy score after being weighed and measured. I was still so cold from the air conditioner, and I held him so close to me to keep him warm. Michael Gene was held by his daddy, then I was brought down to a recovery room. It looked like a dungeon in comparison to the labor and delivery room. Michael was then taken to the nursery. My husband left the hospital soon after.

I was then brought to a shared room with a roommate, this room looked as bad as the recovery room. I thought, "What a cruel joke to be teased with such a beautiful space while in labor and delivery, then dumped into this!"

While in my nice room I was given the option to have Michael stay in my room or the nursery overnight. I wanted him to stay with me. I had been in my room for over an hour when I asked my nurse how long it would be before they would bring him to my room. I began to grow concerned when they wouldn't give me a time. She said the doctor would be in to talk to me. I called my parents' house to talk to my husband, but he had gone home to our condo. Again, this was before we had a cell phone. I had left a message on our house phone for him to call me as soon as he got in. Shortly thereafter, a doctor had come into my room with some kind of a release form. Michael was in distress and was going to be taken to the NICU. "What is a NICU?" I asked.

The answer I received was, "It's Neonatal Intensive Care Unit. We believe your baby has swallowed amniotic fluid and has what is called 'wet lung'."

They wanted to prepare me before they brought Michael in to see me while on their way to the NICU. I think I had gone into shock. I couldn't wrap my thoughts around my baby being in distress. What did that mean? It didn't make sense as he had gotten a high appy score and weighed as much as his siblings did when they were born. My husband had called while a second doctor was in my room. I needed him for support – all this information they were giving me was more than my mind could handle.

There is no doubt that he loves his children. It just seemed to me he couldn't process circumstances out of the ordinary. He was less than sensitive to the challenges that the doctors were preparing me for.

I said, "You need to come back to the hospital now! Something is wrong. Michael is sick!" He told me to stop over-reacting, and that he was tired and would be back later in the day.

I had an urgency for support that I had never experienced before. Emotions of this magnitude are different when your child is sick. I knew how to fight for my life, I didn't know what to do to fight for Michael's life. I was weak with fear, yet I needed to be strong. How? How do I find strength when I am overwhelmed with paralyzing fear? Not to mention, I had just given birth a few hours prior.

I was so angry with my husband. That was the last straw. This was our son, our little helpless baby, and in that moment, I felt no love for my husband. I no longer had empathy for him and was done making excuses for him.

Michael was brought into my room by a team of nurses and a doctor shortly after I hung up the phone with my husband. Our sweet little boy's chest cavity was working so hard to get air, it looked as if each breath he took collapsed his chest into his back. I kissed his beautiful little face and said please take him down there as fast as you can, please help my baby breathe. His chest was pounding with such rapid force.

I was so scared for my baby's life. I cried out with tears that soaked my face… "Please dear Lord, please heal my baby." The rest of my two-day stay was a blur. I couldn't eat or sleep. The first 24 hours were the most critical, and each hour seemed like a day to me. I wasn't even allowed to see him until the morning I was discharged.

I don't remember when my husband showed up. I had no concept of time. For some reason his idea of 'supporting' was based on the false presumption that tough love would build strength in coping with any trauma, much like he did when I was in the burn unit. He would say, "Okay Alicia, time to snap out of it, stop milking this." How silly of me; I wasted so much time burning from the inside out and all I needed to do was to "snap out of it" to be well again! How thoughtless and selfish of me!

God forgive me, but in all honesty, I didn't want to be with him anymore! I wanted to take his tough love approach and shove it up his @$#%^!!!

Michael was in an enclosed isolate. Before entering the NICU we had to go into a sterile room, I washed my hands and forearms, then put on a sterile robe. I was able to put my hands through the rubber gloves that were attached to the enclosed isolate, and I reached in and held his little hand.

I was so grateful my children enjoyed being over my parents' house. It's ironic to think about how badly I wanted out of their home ten years prior and how much time and healing I did there after having SJS. In the words of my longtime friend Sharon, I was having a "do over."

I spent a few hours a day with my children at my parents' house and I slept in a chair in the NICU next to Michael's isolate overnight when they allowed me to.

My husband went to the pharmacy and rented an electric breast pump for me to keep at my parents' house. I guess my body had gone into shock, because I didn't produce milk the first few days I used the pump. I wanted Michael to have colostrum the first time they fed him with the feeding tube. I remember sitting on my parents' bed with the electric pump violating my breast with the suction of a pulsing vacuum. I had only used a hand pump when I had Bianca and Anthony, so this was a new unpleasant experience for me -- until I heard the sound of milk squirting into the cylinder-shaped bottle. I was so happy ... my milk began to flow. I had two three-ounce bottles filled in no time!

I put the bottles in a small lunch cooler with an ice pack and went quickly to the hospital. I had lost so much weight so quickly I didn't even look as if I just had a baby. It seemed like weeks had passed but it had only been three days. There was a different security personnel checking IDs when I arrived. He seemed baffled when he looked at the date of Michael's birth in regard to my thin stature. He then called up to the NICU to confirm my ID before allowing me entry.

I will never forget the panic I felt when I saw the IV in the top of Michael's forehead. I was so upset by how it looked. I did my best to stay composed and asked how long it would be before they would move it to a different place. He was on a C-pack breathing inhaler to support his breathing. Thank God he was doing so much better. He had been moved to an open isolate. The most critical time had passed, and he was in less distress. I sang my prayers in the tune of a soothing lullaby over him, and I held his little hand and stroked him tenderly to comfort both him and me. He was so beautiful, his little face was truly the face of an angel, one who belonged here on earth. I sang to him for hours. It filled me with so much peace and comfort.

The "girls," aka my breasts, would let me know when it was time to give them release. I would sit on a rocking chair in the pumping room at the NICU. There was a refrigerator with small plastic baskets labeled for each pumping mom, and most of them had one or two 3-oz. cylinder-shaped bottles filled 3/4 of the way. After my milk came in, I produced enough milk to feed most of the babies in there! All my bottles were filled to the top, and my basket wasn't big enough to house all of them.

When Michael was six days old, I was able to hold him. He still had an IV and feeding tube. It was so wonderful to feel him in my arms. There had been a storm coming and the staff was busy preparing for a transported baby. She was going to be in the isolate next to Michael. There were only a few yards in between each isolate. The baby girl was only a few ounces over one pound. I overheard the staff say that

102

the mom didn't know she was pregnant until that morning when she went into the hospital with abdominal pain.

That little baby girl was so tiny when she arrived. I held Michael and prayed for that sweet tiny baby. Later that day a storm rolled in. The hospital's generator kicked in when the power in the surrounding building went out. It was so eerie. I didn't want to leave Michael that day, so I stayed at the hospital and ate what became my new favorite candy - a 100 Grand candy bar that I got from the vending machine in the hall outside the NICU.

The baby girl had coded, sometime later that day or night. I had no concept of day or night when I was there, and it seemed as if time stood still and yet passed within moments. It was impossible for me not to see all the effort from the staff to bring her back. She was only a few yards from where I was sitting with Michael. It was the saddest moment to date. I felt such grief for a family I never met. The baby's mom was still recovering in a different hospital. I was also there when the baby girl's dad wheeled the mom into the NICU in a wheelchair. When they put the lifeless infant in her arms, my heart throbbed with pain for them both. I did my best to turn my chair facing away from their view. I was overwhelmed with gratitude concerning Michael, he was no longer critical. However, I felt a tinge of guilt for my joy knowing their pain is one I would never want to know.

Relying on my faith for support, I did my best to balance my time between being at the hospital with Michael and going to my parents' house to be with Bianca and Anthony. One day I walked into my parents' house, Bianca and Anthony ran up to greet me, and I was shocked to see Anthony with a baby bottle in the shape of an old-fashioned soda bottle. Anthony went from nursing to a cup when he was around a year old, and he hadn't used a baby bottle in almost a year. He was so happy to show me what grandma had bought for him! The words that stayed in my head were... "Why did you give him a bottle?!" The answer to my question quickly became obvious to me. When I was in kindergarten my Nana would greet me with a baby bottle of strawberry milk as I got off the school bus. (Am I the only one that thinks it's inappropriate for a five-year-old to have a baby bottle?) After a few deep breaths, I reminded myself of how much my parents were doing for me and how happy my children were to have sleepovers at grandma and grandpa's house, so I chose to share Anthony's excitement with him. Soon after we went back home, Anthony lost interest in the bottle and gave it to his baby brother.

I put photos of Bianca and Anthony in Michael's NICU bassinet. By Day 9 he started nursing and was discharged on June 14. He made a full recovery after 11 days in the NICU. The staff was so wonderful and kind. They wished us well as we hugged our goodbyes. Michael was on his way to meet his siblings in person.

Chapter Twelve
~ Multitasking ~

Bianca and Anthony welcomed their baby brother home wearing their big sister, big brother shirts.

Bianca, Michael, Alicia and Anthony.
Michael's first day home from the hospital

Michael's crib was in the master bedroom, we had outgrown our two-bedroom condo. Michael was such a good baby; however, I don't think I slept for more than three hours total a day for at least two years. Anthony was a high energy twenty-two months old toddler when Michael was born and demanded a great deal of attention. (Recently, Bianca told her now twenty-two-year-old brother, Anthony, that she couldn't wait until he could talk so she could ask him why he was so mean to her. He just laughed).

We had Anthony's second birthday party at the condo. I set up water tables and lots of different outdoor games for all the children. Anthony was a late talker and when he did start to talk his voice was deep and raspy. Bianca and I understood him best and we were his interpreters. He would get so frustrated when he wasn't understood. For example, if he would ask my mom for a glass of milk and she didn't get it for him, he would cross his arms high on his chest, his bottom lip would pop out into a pout, and then he would look up at me with such a sad expression. I would ask, "What's wrong Buddy? (Buddy was the name of endearment I had for him). Why do you look so sad?"

He would reply, "Bu-cuz gama wunt yet me hab muk." Which meant, "Because grandma won't let me have milk." I'm sure she would have gotten it for him if she had understood his request for a glass of milk.

The busyness with my children kept me distracted from my own issues. I always thanked God for all my blessings when I wrote in my journal. Then I would write about how lonely my heart was. My children filled me with so much love and joy, but a lonely heart is different. I wanted to share the joys and challenges of my days with my partner when the house was quiet. That was what my heart longed for. I began to write what I wanted from my marriage. That was one of my biggest challenges to let go. I knew I couldn't stay in a loveless marriage. It was too painful for my spirit, yet I also knew the alternative meant divorce ... and that was against my family's core belief system.

Lack of sleep began to take its toll on my subconscious vulnerability. Thoughts that I had locked away and only shared in my journal began to find release. One example of this spewing of words took place while taking a walk around my complex with Symantha after our children were asleep, and after angrily crunching down on Tums, hoping to get some relief from the ulcerated blisters that pulsed with stinging pain in my mouth. In getting to know each other, she asked, "So tell me about you and Bill."

I unexpectedly blurted out "I'm NOT going to grow old with that S.O.B.," words that I couldn't retract after they escaped my mouth. That was the beginning of a new trend for me. I started giving a voice to the pain that tormented my heart. I was able to justify my insubordination to my core belief system by telling myself, "God didn't keep me alive through the HELL of SJS to live with a tormented heart." I began to reevaluate the belief system that had been set in place over the past thirty years. Some of those beliefs no longer served my heart. Another layer of that onion had been peeled away.

Multitasking brought out my creativity. I played it like a game and set up challenges for myself. I wore Michael like an article of clothing, using the snuggly front pack. As he grew, I carried him on my back in the hitchhiker backpack. I'll never forget going shopping for Bianca's fifth birthday. After her school bus pulled out of our complex, I followed it for the first few miles before heading to the toy store. While shopping, I had Michael in the front pack nestled against my chest. Anthony wouldn't stay in the shopping cart at the toy store, so I held his hand while pushing a full cart of toys out into the parking lot with my opposite hand. Suddenly, Anthony broke free from my hand and ran towards the parking lot. I let go of the cart, cradled Michael with my now free hand, and I ran after Anthony. I was able to scoop him up like a football. I held him to my body as if I was running the ball for the winning touchdown of the Super Bowl. I watched my overflowing cart ricochet off parked cars as it increased speed toward the road. After wrestling Anthony into a car seat and fastening three-month-old Michael into his, I drove over to my cart and retrieved Bianca's birthday gifts. Just another day in the life of a mom! I couldn't believe no one offered me help.

As always, birthdays are special to me. We start the day with a traditional "birthday breakfast." The night before, I decorate the kitchen table with balloons, streamers and a stack of birthday gifts after the birthday child was fast asleep. On the morning of their birthday they would wake to find their favorite breakfast food and a celebration! Bianca's birthday will always be a monumental day for me. It's her birthday coupled with my "second chance at life" anniversary. Sadly, that day also is now grieved by so many. I always keep the devastation of 9/11 in my thoughts and prayers.

Bianca started kindergarten, and she had the afternoon half-day session. I was happy about that. I had a great deal of eye pain along with tormenting mouth sores and horrible heartburn. I was physically ill often, yet I was able to keep it to myself. I enjoyed my children so much … I refused to give in to the pain SJS caused me.

Michael caught a cold that became an upper respiratory infection. We had to go to the pediatrician's office at least once a week. He was given so many different medicines, none of which were able to clear it up. After almost a month of office visits, I called a pulmonary specialist. When I was told we would have to wait two weeks for an appointment, I began to cry while on the phone. I pleaded with the receptionist and told her Michael's medical history. I also told her I hadn't had more than two hours sleep because he had been up coughing all night. After putting our phone conversation on hold, she came back on the line and told me to bring him in at 8:00 AM the next morning. I was so relieved to know he was going to be seen.

That morning, after getting Bianca and Anthony ready to leave the house, I heard Anthony calling out to me from the bathroom. He attempted to stand on the toilet seat to reach his toothbrush, but the lid was up, and his leather work boot got stuck in the drain of the toilet. After rolling up my sleeves, I submerged my hand into the toilet water and tried to pull up on Anthony's ankle to remove his boot. Anthony wrapped his arms around my head for balance. His boot was so tightly wedged in, I had to loosen the laces and pull his foot out of the boot. Never a dull moment in motherhood! It was now 7:00 AM, I had one hour to change Anthony's clothes then drop Bianca off at a classmate's house, and Anthony at my parents' house in order to get Michael to his appointment by 8:00 AM.

The pulmonary specialist's office was at the hospital. Michael had been up coughing all night; my poor baby was so sick. I was three miles from the hospital when I saw the red and blue lights in my rearview mirror. I pulled over. Michael had been coughing so violently, and I hoped the officer could help me get him to the hospital sooner. I told him of my urgency. He then asked for my license and registration, and he informed me I would be getting a ticket for going 32 mph in a 25-mile zone. He then walked away from my vehicle to greet another driver on the opposite side of the road. I was so upset – I got out of my car and told him to send me the ticket in the mail because I had to get my baby to the hospital. I got back in my car and proceeded to the hospital.

Michael was admitted to the children's unit after the doctor saw him. He was diagnosed with pneumonia. After seven days of treatment, he was discharged to go home. I later fought the ticket that I had received in the mail by using Michael's medical records as proof of my urgency. I gloated at bit when the judge reprimanded the officer for his unprofessional and insensitive behavior. Gratefully, I won! No ticket, no court fees!

While Michael was in the hospital, I was able to sleep in a reclining chair next to his crib. I was still nursing him, so I went home while he slept during the day. My mother- in-law stayed at our condo with Bianca and Anthony. One afternoon while my mother-in-law was visiting Michael, we went to the hospital cafeteria. While paying for my lunch, I noticed my pear-shaped engagement ring was no longer on my finger. We looked around the hospital room, as well as under the bed and in the chair cushions. It must have fallen off while giving Michael a sponge bath the night before. I had hoped that if someone found it and chose not to return it, it meant they needed it more than I did.

Michael came home with a nebulizer. When the pneumonia was gone, the specialists believed he might have infant asthma, or worse, cystic fibrosis. I was so frightened and exhausted, the sores in my mouth along with eye pain (due to the ingrown eyelashes that were growing behind my eyelids and scratching my cornea) were a constant reminder of the aftermath of SJS.

I had to go to the eye doctor frequently to have them extracted. Eye pain was relentless, a challenge I continue to live with. I was so grateful to be home with all three of my children. I chose to be thankful. I knew how blessed I was to have our baby home.

Chapter Thirteen
~ Friends ~

Michael required a nebulizer treatment on a three-hour cycle, poor little guy resisted with all his might the first few times. Nursing him after his treatments proved to be effective in consoling both of us. My hair had grown long over the past few years and I frequently wore it in a French braid that fell to one side. After nursing, I would place him in the crib and lean forward to tilt my head toward him. Michael would rub the end my braid between his little fingers to relax himself, or until he drifted off to sleep. I thought maybe if I replaced my hair with a doll's hair, I would no longer have to lean over his crib while he drifted off to sleep. Bianca offered up her Puffy baby doll that was mostly bald with a patch of hair on the top of its head. Bianca's choice was a success. Michael carried that baby around for three years along with his pacifier. The pacifier and doll were referred to as "Nookie-baby."

Symantha had come over one day to help me with Bianca and Anthony. She was always helpful with cleaning up the house for me as well. There are times I couldn't imagine how I could have gotten through the day without her help. Michael had to have three sweat tests to rule out cystic fibrosis. I prayed over my baby with all my heart. After reading the information the doctors had given me to prepare me for the possibility of this disorder, I had a whole new respect and compassion for parents and their children who live with that challenge. I remember being in my bedroom giving Michael a nebulizer treatment – Sym was in the kitchen, Bianca and Sym's boys Nicky and Eric were playing in the kids' bedroom, and Bill was watching TV. The condo was set up with a dining area and living room that opened to the kitchen. There were also two bedrooms and two bathrooms off the main hall. I heard Bill yell, "Alicia! Anthony is crying!" and then I heard Sym yelling at Bill. When all the commotion quieted down, Sym came into my bedroom carrying Anthony in her arms. She was all fired up! She began to tell me how she told Bill off. Apparently, Anthony fell and bumped his head in front of Bill, yet Bill was calling for me to pick him up. My friends always had my back. I was so sad for my little boy's booboo head. Sym and I traded my children so that I could comfort my sweet little boy, while she cradled Michael. I took solace in knowing I had such supportive friends; they emulated a strength I began to embrace.

I didn't write in my journal much in those first few weeks after Michael was discharged from the hospital. I guess I was just too exhausted. However, I do have such wonderful photos and videos of my children and me in the 1990s. Every day was a fun adventure with them. Challenges were always present, though. At that time, the sores in my mouth, dry itchy eyes, and shortness of breath compromised my physical well-being. Emotionally, I knew life with Bill was taking its toll on me, and my relationship with my mom began to revert back to my adolescent years (That was a challenge with lots of layers). All of this empowered me to stay focused on my spiritual journey.

I started looking for a house after the 1st of the year in 1994. The court date for the medical malpractice case was also coming up. I didn't understand why Bill and I didn't have more of a savings in the bank for a house. He earned a good income and took care of paying our bills. We weren't credit card users, and I wasn't one to spend what I didn't budget for. Our parents were willing to lend us money with the understanding that we pay them back after the lawsuit was settled. That put so much pressure on me – what if we didn't win? What if the court thought SJS wasn't real? My fears began taking up space in my already crowded head.

Laura, my friend and cousin's wife, was our real estate agent. She and I weeded through many different houses before I saw the one worth telling Bill about. For him it was love at first sight when he walked down to the full finished basement, equipped with a full-size wet bar, office, and playroom. It also had an in-ground swimming pool. The four-bedroom colonial house sat on a three-quarter acre fenced-in yard. It was across the street from a school, on a road that had traffic from a nearby apartment complex that made it less desirable than a house in a quiet neighborhood; therefore, it was more affordably priced. It was built in the 1980s, and the bedrooms were much larger than those in the new homes that were being built in our town. The price was right due to the housing market at that time; however, we weren't able to sell our condo, so we rented it out. The house needed a fresh coat of paint, some new carpets and a new pool liner. Other than that, the house was in "move-in condition." We joked that the only wood Bill could work

114

with was a #2 pencil, so this house was perfect for our needs because it required little work.

We moved in the summer of 1993. On closing day, Doug, Bill's cousin, and I stayed up all night painting the entire inside of the house while the children and Bill were back at the condo sleeping. Doug and I had so much fun speed-painting. Even though I wore a face mask and protective glasses while painting, the fumes wreaked havoc on my health. I pushed through it and kept my pain to myself.

Subsequently, when Doug came over to visit, he would say, "Spending a day with my children was the best form of birth control." He was in his early twenties and seemed to be amused by the amount of energy our boys had.

Around the same time, Bill's parents had sold his Nana Cecilia and Grandpa Frank's house. They offered us their antique furniture that was no longer being used, and I loved it – not only because it was beautiful, but it had a sentiment connected to it. I didn't have any heirlooms from my grandparents, so I treasured all they had to offer. Our friends shared their support by offering a hand with our move. The 2800 square foot center hall colonial was freshly painted and furnished in just a few days. Bill started to decorate the basement like a sports bar; he was in his glory. I loved that house, mostly because of the memories I have with my children and all the entertaining we did.

I was so happy to live in such a beautiful space. We began to meet our neighbors, and our home quickly became the "go-to" house. I loved to entertain, and I had a dream playroom set up in the basement for the children. Decorating my home truly filled me with joy.

Chapter Fourteen
~ Settlement ~

After hours of being prepped by my two lawyers, I had been experiencing conflict with what I believed had happened to me regarding the SJS/TEN. I believed it started with Motrin, and penicillin exacerbated it. They believed it was just the penicillin. The defense for my family doctor, who was the first one who treated me for this, had offered me a settlement of $500,000.00. My lawyers believed my case was worth over one million dollars, or more. My family wanted me to be taken care of financially due to my health concerns so they encouraged me to go to court and let a jury choose my settlement which could be far more. However, the thought of giving that much power to the unknown created fear in me. What if the jury didn't think I deserve a reward settlement for what I had been through? I had to pay our parents back the money they loaned us for the house – and I had medical expenses as well.

The dialogue I had going on in my thoughts coupled with the post-traumatic nightmares that reappeared sent me into a panic. My fight to keep my spirit moving forward felt threatened. Physically the pain of my burning flesh was long gone, yet healing the memory was a work-in-progress. I didn't have a safe place to go with what was being played out in my mind. For instance, if I lose the case, my spirit will die. What if this group of people thinks I am lying? I felt a level of guilt because I was told to withhold my truth about what I believed happened to me. I felt my body had reacted to one of the over-the-counter medicines that I took before I saw my family doctor, and that the penicillin derivative caused a dual allergic reaction in my body. I was told none of those medicines had proved to cause SJS or TEN. This was so disturbing to me! I pretty much told myself not to bother discussing it again because they might think I don't know what I'm talking about. I knew my family and my lawyers were looking out for me and I'm so grateful for all they were doing. Challenging the pharmaceutical company would have been excruciating for me and at that time I didn't have any evidence to use in my favor. (This is not the case in 2014!) Nor did I have the fight in me to go up against them. So, there was no doubt, my family doctor was on the hook. He misdiagnosed me and prescribed a derivative of the medication that was clearly written on my medical form "ALLERGIC TO PENICILLIN."

It was a chilly morning in March, 1995... court day. The events of the day were focused on me. My friend Karen and former co-worker from DePaolo's Salon arrived to take care of our three children while I was getting ready to leave for the first day of my court hearing. The judge put a two-week estimated trial time on my case. Being away from my children for two weeks didn't sit well with me. Bill and I went to pick my parents up and we then met our lawyers at the courthouse. I saw my doctor walking down the hall with his lawyers. I felt as if all the air had left the building. I needed to walk outside to fill my lungs. My parents, Bill and my lawyers were gathering papers and going over some last-minute preparation while awaiting our expert witness, an infectious disease doctor who was flown in from out of state.

It was surreal considering the six years of countless hours preparing for my day in court – to go face to face with my doctor. This was Day One of at least ten for me to tell my story to a panel of men and women, while my expert witnesses prove my doctor negligently caused my pain and suffering (which in fact he had.)

My lawyer walked me into the empty courtroom, so I'd be familiarized with the setting of the trial. The jury was being considered for my lawyers to then make the final cut. My lawyer opened a Kodak folder containing four sets of 8x10 photographs. He handed me a set of 8 photos and then exited the courtroom to distribute the others to the necessary parties. It had been a few years since I saw the photos of myself in the burn unit, and the photos of my face were blown up to be almost life-size. I then sat back into the wooden bench seat and slowly studied each of the photographs. I then began to feel my body temperature rise into a sweat and my chest became tight and throbbed with pain. It was as if I were looking into the heart of that 26-year old young mother, who was me! I leaned forward and used the back of the wooden bench in front of me for support, almost in a kneeling position. I clasped my fingers together so tightly they became numb. I began to sob, "Dear God, I can't do this. I can't fight anymore. It hurts too much." I could hear the echo of my pain bounce off the walls of the room filled with empty seats. I asked myself, "How can they put a price on the pain I endured? My doctor has no idea of the senseless and excruciating suffering I sustained and continue to live with." I saw flashes of the pain in each of those pictures. My mind flooded with sad memories of having missed the month surrounding my baby girl's first birthday, along with unrelenting pain in my mouth, the loss of my eyesight, and the smell of dried nasal blood and burning skin. It was more than I could handle. I couldn't stop it! My tears were so warm on my face, I feared they would burn me again. I don't know how long it was before I found the strength in my legs to carry me out to the hall. I saw my dad first and told him I couldn't do it. He held me in a protective hug while I cried the words," I can't relive that pain. I want to take the settlement offer and go home." I stayed embraced in my dad's arms until I felt strong enough to stand on my own. I spoke to my lawyers and they reassured me that we had a strong case with all the expert witnesses. Even though the defense sought to remove my burn unit photos from the evidence, my lawyer had won in favor of being able to present them, along with the fraudulent diagnostic report from my doctor in which he changed a diagnosis on my original record. My lawyers had discovered this while reading through my doctor's depositions. My lawyers wanted me to proceed, and they told me that they had rehearsed a plan of cross-examination; they were looking forward to seeing my doctor's reaction when they provided the jury with the proof of him tampering the original evidence.

We discussed in length my desire to settle instead of continuing. The original offer was now off the table and I would have to settle for less, then pay court fees. I told my attorneys I understood my final payment would be considerably lower than what my family wanted for me, and I appreciated their enthusiasm and confidence, but what was happening to me couldn't be measured by money that day. In having to relive those first few weeks triggered pure terror through my entire body. I just couldn't do it. I knew my family was disappointed for me, not just because of the amount I had settled for, but they thought going face to face with my doctor would have given me a sense of peace and closure. I signed many different papers before leaving the courthouse that day. I was relieved it was over and couldn't wait to put it behind me forever. I was confident in the choice I made to settle out of court. The fact of the matter is, I could have lost regardless of all the proof of causation my lawyers had.

On March 15, 1995 after both lawyers took their percentage and the fees were paid, I received a check numbered 103551 as settlement. I was able to pay off the house loans from my dad and my father-in-law, leaving me with less than half of the settlement payout. I invested the balance with a reputable bank, setting aside a budget to buy some fun things for me and the children. First was a wooden swing set and some gifts for my nieces and nephews.

I also lent money to a good friend so she and her husband could buy a home in a safe neighborhood for their two children. They had had a series of unfortunate events in their lives; it gave me such joy to help them. They were so grateful and never missed a payment.

{Due to the economic tragedy, of 2005/2007 my financial profile plummeted; my financial safety net no longer sustains my medical needs}.

Chapter Fifteen
~ Should Have? ~

Writing that last chapter had proven to be difficult for me. So, I shared my challenges and emotional pain with my Wednesday night women's group {These are a group of women I wrote about in my prologue}. Knowing these awesome women have my back makes this healing process possible. I have a better understanding of why it took me over 25 years to write about the cause and effect SJS/TEN had on my life's journey.

Ellen's words embraced me, as if they wrapped around my fear and brought clarity to the emotions that threatened my commitment to keep writing this book. She said, "You are in the belly of the beast."

Then Gayle asked, "Alicia, did you hear that?"

I sat quietly for a moment and replayed her words to myself; the **belly of the beast**, then I came to a sound realization of what that meant for me. Here it was.... the **core** to my **emotional healing** was front and center – **forgiveness**. I went home that night and cried while I wrote in my journal. Awareness of the unknown seems like an oxymoron, nevertheless, I trust God. I asked for guidance and forgiveness, starting with forgiving myself. I don't blame myself for becoming ill, however, I have questioned other choices I've made. Being hard on myself doesn't serve me and it's not effective or productive in any sense. Believing I failed has kept me from achieving my goals! At times, I thought I should have been stronger, or should have challenged the pharmaceutical / distributors of Motrin and Tylenol – not for myself but for others. I felt so sad and tormented thinking how many others have blindly suffered the pain of SJS/TEN. I then wrote something Gayle said to me: "Don't 'should' all over yourself" (referring to "shit" as "should"). She always has a way with shifting language into a healing opportunity. I have even made peace with my family doctor – forgiving others is quintessential in emotional healing.

I sometimes question how differently my case would have played out if today's information was available 25 years ago. Is it possible that I was right (in 1989) about what was happening to my body? Giving a voice to that 26-year-old mother in my heart is so healing for me, by sharing my experience and my perspective to those who are willing to listen. Perhaps it would bring awareness to prevent others from suffering the devastation of this horrific drug-induced reaction.

Stevens-Johnson Syndrome and TEN are not new. It has been taking lives for decades. I wouldn't be surprised if there were countless death certificates that state "Cause of Death: UNKNOWN." When perhaps it could have been "Cause of Death: Stevens-Johnson Syndrome" or "TEN." To all the victims before me, those who lost their lives in such a traumatic way, this book is to bring awareness, so they did not pass in vain. This devastating and potentially deadly reaction deserves more recognition, more research, more awareness, and most of all, more education. Still today, medical professionals don't easily identify or recognize the symptoms to effectively diagnose for early intervention. I still, in 2014, have to explain and describe SJS to doctors and other medical professionals. Recently, I was prescribed medications that I have charted to be allergic to! We must be our own vigilant advocates, and advocates for our loved ones that are unable to do it for themselves. Thankfully, SJS and TEN have recently been getting some media attention, and warnings have been posted on over-the-counter medications. Without a doubt, knowledge is power. My hope is not only for early detection, it's also for the possibly of preventive testing.

Researching Stevens-Johnson Syndrome on the internet provides a slew of information, the latest research, along with survivor stories, as well as memorials.

Two of the websites I have searched are:

https://medsites.mc.vanderbilt.edu

https:/www.mayoclinic.org/diseases-conditions/SJS

Chapter Sixteen
~ Changes ~

Once the settlement was behind me, I began to re-evaluate my life and my core belief system. It was time to change what was no longer working for me. The things I loved doing most evolved around my three children. I became a CCD teacher for Bianca's class at our church, I volunteered in my children's elementary school, and participated with the Girl Scouts as well as Cub Scouts. Keeping busy was an understatement. I truly loved what I was doing, but I also knew I used 'keeping busy' as a distraction from the things that weren't working, such as my marriage. I thought I was doing a great job keeping my secret from my new neighbors until one morning at the children's bus stop. My husband abruptly handed off our son to me then quickly turned and walked back to our house. One of my neighbors made a comment. She said, "Your husband reminds me of my ex-husband... notice that I said EX."

I thought, 'Oh no, our cover is blown!'

Not long after, I asked Bill to see a marriage counselor with me. I made the appointment, with a babysitter in place for the children. When he didn't show up for our first appointment, I utilized my time by making small talk with the therapist. Bill did show up for the second appointment and proceeded to voice how he felt under attack and concluded that counseling wasn't for him. My experience was quite the opposite; Amy, the therapist, offered me a safe space to share my feelings. I then decided to schedule weekly appointments with her and utilize the one-hour-per-week sessions to focus on me. I didn't have much to say about SJS. I wanted to put the painful memories attached to it behind me. The daily eye pain and other health-related issues not in my control were enough of a reminder. Over the next few months, I gave myself permission to be honest with what went on behind closed doors – in my past and present. Defying what I had been told about going to "therapy" empowered me, no longer believing I was "weak-minded." Surviving SJS taught me how strong I am. I now know it takes great strength and humility to ask for help, and God knows those past six years gave me my share. I took "baby steps." Amy recommended a few books for me, one of which was a Melody Beattie book, *Codependent No More*. I had never heard the term 'codependent,' and I didn't think we had addiction issues in our family. Nevertheless, I trusted her, I was willing to be open to what she was offering.

After reading all the recommended books, saying I had a life-changing epiphany would be an understatement. Soon after, I began seeing more clarity in how my past played out in my present. Having the capability to love and share kindness was a reflection of my family. There are many other positive qualities of family values that will always hold strong in my heart. On the flip side, there was misplaced criticism, fear, shame and guilt, and the will to work on not passing that inheritance on to my children became my mission.

Much like focusing on the need to stay alive through the pain of SJS, I reached deep into my emotional vulnerability. Knowing our three children could one day emulate the dysfunction of our marriage in their lives gave me the will to learn as much as I could, hoping to better enable myself to change the dynamic that was obviously not working. The thought of our children choosing emotionally unavailable relationships, or them becoming disconnected from their emotions, empowered me to push through the fear.

Clarity and validation came to me through reading self-help books and writing in my journal. It seemed what I needed most coincidentally showed up. I looked forward to watching The Oprah Winfrey Show. At times she would have a guest that supported my mission. It could have been a doctor, an author, or someone just sharing their story of triumph over tragedy – all of which supported my spiritual journey. To me Oprah Winfrey offered healing opportunities to those who were open to receive them. She has been instrumental in my life and countless others.

In the midst of things, I continued to keep up with my day-to-day routine, keeping busy with the children and visiting with my girlfriends while our children played together was enjoyable for me. One afternoon my friend, Janet, was over for a play date with her two children. She and I were sitting in my kitchen at our octagon-shaped counter, accompanied by six counter stools. It doubled as our kitchen table. We were chatting over a cup of tea when Bill came home from work. He flew around the kitchen snatched up our half-full cups of tea, cleared our plates of food, wiped the crumbs that were left behind, then stormed into the family room yelling to the children to pick up and put away the toys they were playing with. He then disappeared into his man-cave in our basement. His wrath left a clean kitchen and five crying children in its wake. Janet looked at me and said, "If you never do anything else for yourself again, go to the weekend family awareness program." I was baffled by her recommendation. She defined it for me, and suddenly a vivid awareness came over me. (I had an "Aha!" moment).

Anxiously, I showed up ten minutes early for my appointment with Amy that week. I had all this new information I had received from reading about codependency, along with an enlightening confession from Janet about her recent life experiences. I was bursting at the seams to tell Amy what I had discovered: "I'm codependent!!" – As if I won a prize I didn't want. Amy had a big job ahead of her. I was so confused. How was I identifying with all the information I was reading on codependency? Amy supported the idea that I should attend that family program. I was open to it, yet I had lots of excuses that justified why I couldn't go.

The tension in our house was beginning to reflect on my physical health. It took so much time and energy to deflect the negative energy Bill had. He was either in the basement or complaining about things that were out of my control. Friends of ours were visiting one day and witnessed Bill's interaction with me; they both voiced their concerns, addressing Bill's behavior as inappropriate. I had fallen back into old habits of making excuses for his behavior, telling my friends and family his mood swings were due to diabetes … "his blood sugar must have been too high or too low." Bill and I knew this couple before they were married. She then told me that Bill should go for help, and in her opinion, he had issues far beyond diabetes. The weekend after their visit I made the decision to go to attend the free weekend Family Informational Program.

Hovering thoughts of my mom's fear of driving usually kept me from driving to unfamiliar towns by myself. On this particular day, I managed to push those threatening fears away. I selected calming music on the radio, and within 35 minutes I found myself in the parking lot of the Foundation. This was a free, educational workshop geared to support the families who had loved ones in the programs. I followed the schedule that was given to me at the door. It ran from 10:00 AM until 3:00 PM, on both Saturday and Sunday. The sign-in sheet had a space for the attendee's name and the name of patient you were there to visit. I felt like a fraud. Most of the people in there were seeking support to help their loved ones. I still had no clue on how this could possibly benefit me. I was going on blind faith and trusting Amy and my friends. I watched the short films, listened to the lectures and sat in the discussion groups. Before the day was over, I was told I should attend six consecutive weekends. The educational program is set up to run on a six-week schedule. I left that day thinking perhaps Amy and Janet must have misunderstood my situation, because this program definitely wasn't for me!

Bill and I had bought our first computer in 1996. One of Bill's coworkers came over to install it and taught me the basics. The day before my lesson, I had a shipment of our school's "Spirit Day" apparel delivered to our house. I was involved with our school PTA. A few other moms had come over to separate the logo apparel by individual orders so the children could wear their school mascot shirts to the Spirit Day assembly the following day. Most of the orders were completed before they left. I said I'd finish it up separating them by class and dropping them off to the classrooms the next morning before school.

After cleaning up dinner, checking homework, baths and getting the children to sleep, I was awake more than half the night sorting, checking and rechecking to be sure each child received what they ordered. After less than a few hours of sleep, I packed up my minivan and left Bill in charge of getting our children on the bus. The apparel mission was accomplished. There were a few bumps along the way, however, I was so relieved to be finished. When I returned home, I was exhausted.

I had to return to the school for the assembly later that morning, so I was pressed for time. Bill and his coworker had the computer up and running. I sat for a little over an hour and learned how to turn it on and shut it down using the mouse. He also set up an email account for me. That was the extent of my comprehension that day. After a quick cup of coffee, I returned back to the school in time for our spirit rally. To my surprise, I was awarded with recognition for my contributions leading up to and including the event. When

130

our three children returned home from school, we planned on taking them to Stewart's for dinner before gymnastics class. Our neighbor's daughter was with us as well. As we pulled up to the restaurant, Bill asked me to explain to him the process of turning the computer on and off. I answered by saying I was so tired I couldn't explain it at the moment, but I would show him when we returned home. He then went off onto a screaming tangent, telling me I was stupid and that I wasted his friend's time. He threatened me and said that I'm never to touch the computer. He was frightening me and the children. He told them we were going home, and we weren't going to have dinner. I asked him to stop the van and let us out. The children started crying and he continued to yell at them for crying. Again, I asked him to stop the van and let us out. When he refused, I threatened to jump out of the van and call the police. He underestimated my need to keep my children safe. I did as I said I would – I opened the van door while it was moving, and he began to slow down in the parking lot of Stewart's. I jumped out when I believed it to be safe and ran to the phone booth. I closed the door keeping my foot firm on its hinge so it couldn't be forced open from the outside. Bill pulled up next to the phone booth, got out of the van and tried to pull the door open, saying he was sorry. He pleaded with me not to call the police. I then began to bargain with him, stating if he dropped the keys and walked to the far side of the parking lot I wouldn't call. He conceded to the compromise. When I saw he was far enough away I opened the phone booth door, picked up the keys, jumped into the minivan and locked the doors. The children were crying for me not to leave their daddy behind. I put the car in park and did my best to console them. I honored their request by pulling up to Bill. I agreed to let him into the car after he apologized. The trauma of that night caused me to rethink the judgment I made regarding the family program at the Foundation. When Bill went back to his three 12-hour day weekend shift and my CCD teacher commitment was completed for the year, I was able to have a babysitter stay with the children on Saturday. I made the six-week commitment to the family program.

Chapter Seventeen
~ Fine ~

Six weeks of attending the family program turned into eight. I was learning so much about myself by listening. I was willing and committed to making a change in my life. Gayle Potter was the facilitator of the weekend program. It took weeks before I spoke in the group room and I preferred just listening. One day Gayle looked my way and asked me how I was doing. I don't remember my reply, however I do remember her asking what life was like for me in my family. When I answered that it was fine, she said, "FINE" as in **F**'ed-up-**I**nsecure-**N**eurotic-**E**mpty?" An acronym I had never heard before and I was at a loss for words.

Weighing in at no more than 105 pounds, standing no more than 5 feet tall, this powerhouse of a woman had more gusto and heart than anyone I have ever met. Her purpose was to tell it like it is, and she takes her business of educating as a matter of life and death. In that moment I knew I was exactly where I needed to be.

My family was supportive when I told them what I was doing. I shared what I was learning about codependency with them and my friends. It seemed like I opened up a can of worms. It was brought to my attention that at least two of my childhood friends and two of my relatives had similar challenges, one of which was my friend Ryan. He and his wife had visited us before their second child was born, and again after. I was shocked to hear from his sister that he and his wife were preparing to file for divorce. The "don't talk, don't tell" motto began to fall apart for me – it seemed the more I talked openly without judgment or shame, the more my friends and family did the same – and I felt so relieved.

I spoke with my family about the concerns I had. I even invited my parents and siblings to attend a Saturday educational family day with me to get their point of view. Having my parents and siblings accompany me was comforting, the day was going well until we went into the cafeteria for lunch. My mother began to rage, accusing me of orchestrating all the people who had attended that day as a plot against her. As the volume of her voice raised, I felt as if I was shrinking into a frightened child. I ran out of the cafeteria and found the group room Gayle was facilitating. I opened the door, entered, sat in a chair and cried with my hands covering my face as my head reached to my knees in the pose of a child hiding with fear. Peeling back another layer of the "onion," flashes swept through my mind of being in the crossfire of the screaming verbal matches that transpired between my mom and Nana and then my mom redirected to me. As a child, I ran into the woods in the back of our house with our family dog, or up the street to a neighbor's house. Perhaps running into the group room to find safety was no different. Overwhelmed with emotion, I spoke to Gayle wondering if this is what a breakdown could feel like. Her words to me were, "No, Alicia, you are experiencing a break-THROUGH, not a break-DOWN. In order to heal your past, you must break-THROUGH the fear of those memories."

When I started writing my story back in March 2013, my intention was to share my naked vulnerability while in the burn unit, hoping to bring awareness to SJS/TEN and its effects. I did NOT anticipate exposing the vulnerability of my youth, nor did I consider baring the rawness of my sequential healing process. Perhaps this is the depth of healing that I was meant to experience. Healing body, mind and spirit.

Gayle recommended a 5-day codependency program located in Wernersville, PA. It was designed for family members of patients first. I thought, "why should I have to do this work – I'm not the one with the issues." After confiding in Amy, I began to see how suppressed I had become. On the surface, I had showed up as a happy wife with the storybook family – the big beautiful home, two new cars in the driveway, the fairytale marriage. I had no idea what 'normal' was, my life had become so distorted from illusions. The 5-day workshop would allow me necessary time away to focus on myself. However, I didn't want to be away from my children. It was all so perplexing for me to consider how the family around me was so dysfunctional. The realization of these issues and its effect on me were front and center. I knew my marriage was unraveling the day of our 4th anniversary in 1989, while in the burn unit. I had even said I didn't want to grow old with such a negative man. But this was real, it was happening, and I was wondering how our children could be affected if Bill and I divorced. I knew few adults who came from divorced homes and none of them had anything good to say about it. I felt shame and sadness.

I remembered what someone said at the family program – "in case of emergency on an airplane, always take the oxygen first and THEN give it to your child, because if you're not breathing, you can't help them." Although it defied what I believed, their statement made sense. I was so accustomed to giving of myself, I didn't consider the importance of giving to myself. I learned that all behavior both positive and negative are recycled in the family, it was clear that my children and I were already affected by this troubling dynamic, and all of it prompted a clear choice of what I needed to do.

Ready to go yet reluctant to attend, my dad and I spoke openly for the first time in years while he drove me to Pennsylvania.

I was overwhelmed from emotional exhaustion and shame. I thought if nothing else comes from this experience, perhaps I would be able to get some rest. Well, that didn't happen. Let me start by saying it was as if God hand-picked us individually, then brought us together as a group – enabling us to bring buried memories to the surface. It was the third most powerful emotional and spiritual experience I've ever had (after giving birth to my children, and the day I was told I would "live for the son" before being airlifted to the burn unit in 1989). The events of that 5-day stay exposed depths of my soul. The metaphorical description that best describes my experience is that I felt as if I had "open soul" surgery, which exposed all aspects of my life – the good, the bad and the ugly. Then, I was closed up and sent home to heal and do whatever I chose with the information I received. My discharge prescription was to attend at least two 12-step codependency, ACOA (adult children of ...) and/or Al-Anon meetings per week for at least six months and making a standing weekly appointment with Amy.

Now that my children are grown, they don't even remember that I was away from them for five days. Pushing through shame and changing a lifetime of learned behaviors is worth the end result. I know "putting on the oxygen mask first" has transformed the dynamic for the future of my family. I set out on a mission 25 years ago and I am still committed to my cause. I have no doubt that my will and strength have been gifted to me through the blessings of surviving SJS and my three children.

From that point on, my life began to evolve in a way I had not been prepared for. Within the next year I filed for divorce. Bill moved into my parents' house until our condo tenants lease was up. As dysfunctional as it was for Bill to be living with my parents, it gave me peace of mind to know my parents were present when the children were with him. I attended the 12-step support groups on the days Bill had our children. For income I set up childcare in my home for friends and neighbors' children. Two of the children I cared for were my friend's children. He and his wife had separated, she moved out of state, he had custody of their four-year-old and eighteen-month-old children. My heart wanted to be with him so badly, and I truly believed he was going to be my "happily ever after." Knowing he was new into his recovery process raised some red flags for me.

Some frequent questions I heard family members ask while in the group room were:

Q: When do you know when the troubled person is lying?

A: Every time their lips are moving.

Q: Is it ok to start a new relationship?

A: No new relationships for at least one year.

I was also informed of the statistics, one of which is that relapse happens most frequently in the first year. I rebutted all of the red flags by telling myself that Ryan wouldn't risk losing his children, nor would he lie to ME. After all, our relationship wasn't new, it had only been detoured for a decade.

My heart justified my impaired judgment that all would be fine because we were "just old friends," like I said... It was FINE, changing that acronym to "**F**'ed-up-**I**llusion- **N**eedy-**E**motional."

It wasn't long before the statistics proved themselves. To say my heart broke would be an understatement. The pain I felt when I knew I had to detach myself from Ryan and his children felt like a death. Every ounce of my being wanted to rescue him from the demonic repercussions of his challenges, and it took such self-discipline. I have dozens of journals dated from 1997 to 2001 filled with tears and endless prayers, pleading for him to get well and for my heart to heal. Love wasn't supposed to hurt that badly. I had to learn the difference between what was real and what was an illusion. When I was in the burn unit, my heart was so lonely from not getting the love and affection I needed from Bill. I began to believe Ryan was my soul mate. I based all my dreams and illusions on what I felt when he visited me in the burn unit telling myself he would complete my life someday. There were days I was so devastated I didn't think the pain would end. I made a commitment not to have contact with him for at least one year. At first, I had to commit one day at a time, as the weeks passed. It did get easier. In time I began to understand and respect the courage, faith and discipline it takes to fight addiction. Utilizing the 12-step program along with focusing on my family helped.

One of the first things I did after Bill moved out was adopt a kitten and we named her Katie. I had grown up with pets as far back as I can remember – dogs, cats and hamsters. My first cat was gifted to me on my seventh birthday and we named her Melissa Jane, Missy for short. She was an indoor cat and not very social. When I was around nine years old, while on Spring break, I found two abandoned kittens in a wood pile behind a neighbor's house. I emptied my Easter basket replacing the candy with a bath towel and brought the kittens home. My dad bought pet bottles at Two Guys department store and we hand fed them until they grew healthy enough to eat on their own. Those were some of my fondest childhood memories.

One of our cats went on to have three litters. We called her "Momma Cat," and she was the sweetest gentlest cat – even people who weren't fond of cats liked Momma Cat. We found homes for all of her kittens and kept one. I found such comfort in our pets, they love unconditionally. We had a family dog as well, a Germen-Shepherd. He was so gentle and kept us protected for over 15 years before he passed, and our cats were with us for over seventeen years. Our pets were more like family members. Adopting our cat Katie was a gift to my children and to the little girl in my heart.

I vividly remember when a neighbor's child whom I cared for was sent home with a note alerting parents there was a lice outbreak in the classroom. Needless to say, those nits nestled warmly into my children's heads within two days! That is one of the most violating and offensive skin-crawling experiences a parent could go through. I had to spend an exorbitant amount of time and money to destroy those vile insects. Spending more than six hours of combing, washing and rinsing until all signs of those mini monsters were banished from their hair. Soon after my mission was accomplished, I heard a car beeping in my driveway. It was Bill coming to pick up three clean, lice-free children for the weekend with him at my parents' house, while I was left to bag up all their stuffed animals in order to suffocate any remaining lice or eggs, not to mention washing curtains, sheets, towels and blankets, along with vacuuming carpets and furniture. As if that wasn't horrifying enough, one of the kids left the back door open and Katie (our indoor kitten) ran outside. Simultaneously, the phone rang, it was my dad asking me if Bill left my driveway yet because my mom wanted to time the pasta so it would be cooked by the time he arrived with the kids! Seriously?! After hanging up the phone, I leaned up against my kitchen wall, slowly sliding down to the floor as I began to sob. After a good hearty cry lasting at least twenty minutes, crying out, "Why is my life so challenging?" Addressing my faith, "what happened to

the promise I wouldn't be given more than I could handle?"
Later that evening, my friend Karen R invited me for a wine
and cheese girls' sleepover along with two former co-
workers. It was just what I needed. When I arrived home the
next morning, Katie was waiting on the front steps. Thank
Goodness! I was so relieved to see her. I had taken her to the
vet a few weeks later to have her 'fixed,' however that didn't
happen. Her night out turned out to be a night on the town!
We were going to have kittens!

Chapter Eighteen
~ Promises ~

Wednesday nights were Bill's nights with our children and my night to do something for me. Humbly, I accepted an offer to attend a women's group Gayle had been facilitating for years. I showed up feeling so small and vulnerable – my world had been turned upside down, my heart was broken, and my fairy tales had all gone up in flames. There were days I left this group of women feeling so empowered, writing in my journal how wonderful they are. Then, there were days I was in the "hot seat" being confronted while in denial. I swear Gayle could read me like a book. Maybe I liked being in denial, which gave way to another acronym: DENIAL - **D**on't **E**ven **K**now **I** **A**m **L**ying. There were times I wanted to run out screaming. In my journal I would refer to them as "F'ing recovery queens!" Venting…how none of them know what they're talking about! I even wrote a top ten list of why I should stop attending. But it turned out that 99.9% of the time they were spot on! Those are the times Gayle would so eloquently say, "You're just having an "**AFGO**," Alicia".

Here we go again… and just what is an AFGO?

"**A**nother **F**-ing **G**rowth **O**pportunity," she answered.

The life lessons I received from Gayle's Wednesday-night women's group were like being re-parented in a healthy family (not to knock my parents as they are the most loving and generous people I know). These women all offered me so much support while I developed into a strong and independent woman, yet still a work in progress!

While preparing for our divorce, I read a number of books. One was Roger Crawford's; *How High Can You Bounce?* He wrote about writing your own scripted screenplay as a method to realize certain situations in your life, such as job interviews and other major life events. So, I did just that. I wrote in my journal about what I wanted in the final settlement of my divorce. Another book I read was Louise L. Hay's, *You Can Heal Your Life.* I'm pretty sure I bought that book after watching Oprah. I noticed a wart on my ring finger after taking my wedding band off. Curious to see what Louise Hay had to say about warts, I looked it up and on page 207 I found:

Problem: Warts.
Probable Cause: Little expressions of hate.
                         Belief in ugliness.

New Thought Pattern: I am the love and beauty of life in
                          my full expression.

I just laughed and thought, "I couldn't make this stuff up!" Sad, yet true, I was so angry with Bill that I would hum the tune from late 1960s song, *More Today than Yesterday*, changing the lyrics in my head to: "I hate you more today than yesterday, but not as much as tomorrow." "Hate," replacing the word "love" from the original version. I've come to the realization that my anger was misplaced; in fact, what I hated was what he represented at that time – the failure of my "storybook" marriage. I wasn't happy with myself. I wrote about the rage and inappropriate verbal lashing directed to him when our children were present. That was my biggest regret, and what I wanted so desperately to change. He didn't deserve that and neither did our children.

Now that Bianca, Anthony and Michael are adults I totally support them in healing the damage I may have caused. Parenting is not an easy task.

When divorce court day had arrived, my father and sister, Gina, came with me. It wasn't going as well as I had hoped. My sister told me to take what he offered and settle. During a court recess, I went to a pay phone, picked it up to make a collect call to Gayle. Before the operator came on, I heard Gayle's voice saying, "Hello." Apparently, she had just picked up her phone to make a call and we connected without ringing. I believed that was a divine intervention. We talked briefly. I told her what was going on and that I was feeling bullied by Bill and his lawyer. She asked me what I wanted, and then reminded me I had choices. I felt so grounded after our phone conversation. When it was time to go back into arbitration, I did what Gayle suggested – I held my ground and showed up confident and unintimidated. When the judge read the final ruling, it was as if he was reading the script I wrote in my journal. We shared joint custody, and I was appointed the custodial parent. The house remained mine, while Bill was granted the condo. The promise of our vows had sadly come to its end.

Early that summer, Bill brought the kids to the Jersey shore for a few days. While they were gone, Katie gave birth in Bianca's closet to five kittens. I cleaned everything up and set up a kitty nursery in the closet for them to feel safe and cozy. Upon their return, seeing the excitement in Bianca, Anthony and Michael's faces when they laid eyes on those tiny kittens was such a gift for me. I was able to relive the joy I had as a child and share it with my children. Those are the moments I knew God was saying, "Trust me, I promise I will never leave you."

Reading and revisiting the events of my life has become so healing for me. It's a reminder that no matter how difficult a situation might seem, it will pass.

The protocol for attending 12-step groups is to find a sponsor – someone who is the same sex and has a few years' experience in the program. The first time I spoke to Anita, I felt a connection with her. It took me a few weeks to ask her to sponsor me. Going to the meetings was very humbling. Even though it didn't make sense to me at first, I figured it would be something for me to do while Bill had the kids. When I first attended, I wore a hat and sat with my head down, mostly listening while holding back my tears. After each session, I wrote in my journal about how it seemed as if God was present in those rooms, and how peaceful I was beginning to feel. I began looking forward to each meeting. Anita was so wonderful – she had been attending these meetings for years. She was in her mid-sixties and grew up in a conservative Jewish family. She was married and had a strained relationship with her daughter. Like me, she didn't drink or use any substances.

Anita would address me by saying, "Alicia darling…" It had musical sound to it. She invited me to lunch for my 34th birthday at the country club she and her husband belonged. It was the first time I dressed up, put on makeup, and went out as a single woman. She always encouraged me to take care of myself, while being a good mother. She helped me understand that I could do both! Her guidance and love were so comforting. Soon after our lunch date, Anita was diagnosed with terminal cancer that had spread throughout her body, I was devastated by her news.

When my body began recovering from SJS, I didn't have the means to heal the grief of my emotions; that was no longer the case, especially in my expressions of grief. I had learned not to repress my feelings, which allowed me to grieve Anita's death. Anita's passing opened a padlocked sadness, another layer of the metaphorical onion is being peeled away.

After Anita's funeral, I wrote about how much I missed my friend's mom, who had passed away when I was 17. She embodied the image of the loving, nurturing mom I inspired to be. I considered her my "second" mom. I felt like it would have been selfish of me to grieve her death because I needed to be supporting my friend in her grief. Their family lived on our street, and our parents were friends. Her home was the safe house I ran to when I needed refuge from the screaming matches in my childhood home.

Her license plate simply read; *"The M"* – It stood for "The Mom." She was a gentle, loving mother, she was always honest with me, and I had such respect and admiration for her. Her name was Rose, and I later named my daughter Bianca Rose after her. At times, I still feel M's presence around me, finding comfort in the afghan she made for me before she lost her 10-year fight against cancer in 1981. Her eldest daughter is like a sister to me; she is the friend that picked up Bianca for me the morning I was stricken with SJS.

I chose to welcome these awareness's as an opportunity to grieve and heal more productively than I ever had. Anita was the final piece in the process of learning and growing out of the sad, ineffective emotions of my teenage self.

Before Anita passed away, she encouraged me to go to an 80th birthday party for one of the men in our group. We had planned to go together, the kids were with Bill, but she wasn't feeling well enough physically, and I was feeling so low that day that I didn't want to get out of bed. Her persistence won me over. I would get there late, however, I pulled myself out of bed, put on the same black dress I wore to the country club, and off to Princeton I went. I forgot the invitation at home, so I was going on memory. The homes were beautiful, and I saw balloons attached to a mailbox blowing in the air, so I parked my car and walked up the driveway into someone's opened kitchen door. I didn't recognize anyone, so I walked out and asked a small group of men if they knew where Walter was. One replied, "No, but I could be Walter." Oh, my goodness! I was at the wrong house! That was, by far, one of my most embarrassing moments. The sound of my heeled shoes clicking over the little wooden bridge to exit the driveway echoed in my head as I walked over it. I couldn't get to my car fast enough. I drove to the end of the street and was waved in by familiar faces that recognized me and my minivan. That was a day I won't soon forget!

A new school year had begun. Bianca was in third grade, Anthony started kindergarten and Michael went into preschool two days a week, and I went back to work in the salon. It was my first time back after 7 years of recovering from SJS. I continued to volunteer at the kids' school, Girl Scouts, and Cub Scouts. With all that was going on in my life and heart, I was still able to master the ability of compartmentalizing my emotions while enjoying motherhood to the fullest. Working outside the house while parenting was a challenge of trial and error. We grew and learned together. The boys had so much energy that I thought when they became adults, they wouldn't know how to get through a day without being physical with each other. Bianca enjoyed school and made friends very quickly. I managed to keep life as balanced as possible for myself and them. At night we would sit on the bed and the children and I would take turns talking about our day and feelings. Listening to them gave me so much insight into what the divorce meant to them. One night after our divorce was final, I told them we would always be a family and the divorce was only about their Dad and me. I encouraged them to jump up and down on my king-sized bed yelling, "IT'S NOT MY FAULT!" They jumped and yelled until one by one their tired little bodies fell asleep. There's such joy in watching my children peacefully sleeping. I wanted so badly to be a good parent so they would grow into healthy and happy adults.

Working in the salon began to wreak havoc on my health. My eyes were affected the most. I remember sitting on my couch in our family room crying with eye pain after the children were asleep. I was startled when I heard Michael ask, "Mommy, why are you crying?" I had never spoken about my illness with my son until that night. As gently as I could, I told him my eyes hurt because I had an allergic reaction to medicine when Bianca was almost one year old. I said that sometimes I get sad because my eyes hurt so badly. Then I remind myself of how lucky I am that I didn't die. This almost four-year-old boy held my hand and said, "I'm glad you didn't die, Mommy, but if you did, we would still be together. You would have come back to be my daughter instead of me being your son."

I was at a loss for words. Then I said, "Yes, Michael, we would." Holding him in my arms I told him I love him with all my heart. I thank God every day that he is my son.

Going to the eye doctor became a weekly routine. The dryness in my eyes and with the eyelashes that grew behind my lids caused me such pain. After a couple rounds of having them cauterized, along with several attempts to probe and plug my tear ducts to help with the dryness, it was unsuccessful in giving me relief. The damage to my eyes caused them to be lined with scar tissue. Furthermore, dust or poor air quality irritates them. I called an Eye & Surgical

Center in Pennsylvania. They are a team of eye doctors I saw when I first came home from the burn unit. That doctor, recommended electrolysis in my upper and lower eyelids. He explained the procedure: he would insert a fine probe into the hair shaft, then use an electric current to burn out the hair follicle with the hopes that it would not grow back.

I was willing to try anything that could help. When my eyelashes grow behind my lids, they scratch my cornea. It's like having a sharp eyelash stuck in your eye all the time. The constant opening and closing of my eyelids are excruciating. My friend Jake offered to drive me to the procedure. He tried to lessen my fear by saying he was "Driving Miss Daisy." I did enjoy the luxury of his new car and brand-new flip phone. The doctor was very kind and considerate with regard to my anxiety. Similar to the way a dentist injects local anesthetic in preparation for dental work, the doctor pushed the needle in and out repeatedly along both my upper and lower eyelids. The Novocain shots caused stinging, burning pain. As if that wasn't bad enough, I had to keep my eyes wide open as I watched that tormenting needle. Then came the pressure of the probe followed by the pungent smell of burning flesh and displaced eyelashes. I had a whole new perspective of the childhood promise to "cross my heart and hope to die, stick a needle in my eye." I never meant that literally, but here I was having needles stuck in my eyelids. I left the office that day after having only one eye done because I couldn't withstand any more pain. My eye was swollen and bruised.

Before scheduling my next round of hell, I asked my doctor if there was an oral medicine, I could try for my next visit instead of the Novocain shot. He gave me a Xanax for Round 2 a few weeks later. That made me feel dopey and in pain. By Round 3, I 'white-knuckled it.' I held onto the armrest of the chair while the smell of burning eyelash hair permeated my sinuses. Trying to focus on anything other than the pain, I was able to get through it without the Novocain shots or Xanax. When the doctor finished, my hands were so numb from squeezing the armrest that my fingers and knuckles were white. Jake was so gracious – he had scheduled a one-hour massage for me after my procedure was completed. Sadly, within a year that excruciating experience was a 'fail.' Apparently, the scar tissue caused by SJS created a deformation with the hair follicle in my eyelids. My eyelashes found refuge behind my lids once again. I continued to use numbing eye drops, ointments, and eye lubricants for temporary relief in between frequent local eye doctor visits to have them extracted with very fine-tipped forceps, in layman terms, tweezers.

Chapter Nineteen
~ Journals ~

"Dear Lord and Angels,
     Thank you for the many blessings in my life ..."

(Is what I write on each new page of my journal.)

Ironic as it may seem, while reading a journal dated, 1990, I discovered this wasn't the first time I wanted to share my story. I wrote:

"My spirit has endured a great deal; it's time to enjoy the life God intended for me. My body endure physical pain to stay alive. My mind endures emotional pain to find my true self. I'm done with pain. I will share my journey with the world someday. It may or may not be in my lifetime, nevertheless my story will be told, hoping to share my faith with others going through the same thing. We may not know it, but we all have the power to see beyond our challenges and live the awesome life God intended for each and every one of us."

WOW! That was deep. I didn't remember writing that. It's strange, I wrote it ten years after surviving SJS, and here I am sharing my story almost 25 years later in gory detail.

The physical, emotional and spiritual experience I had as a result of surviving transformed my life. I came to realize the cause and effect that it's had on my children as well.

One night in 1998 after the children and I had been to visit our chiropractor, Dr. David Potter informed me that Bianca had had a "release of energy" while being adjusted. In truth, I had no idea of what that meant. He then proceeded to tell me that she may have unsettled emotions. I wasn't sure I understood what that meant, so I just thanked him. Later that night after the children and I were in bed, I heard Bianca crying. I went into her room and sat next to her to comfort her, and she began to talk while in a deep sleep. She said, "It's not fair. You have a different face, a face the boys don't know, and the music stopped!" I laid next to her and cradled her through her tears. At that moment I knew exactly what was happening. When I met Dr. David, he had explained how emotions could become trapped in the nervous system. The work he does helps to release it. When I was pregnant with Bianca, I bought a small red Fisher Price tape recorder with a microphone attached to its side, and a music cassette, *Lullaby Magic*. I played it every night while I was pregnant with her and I played it for her after she was born, singing along as she peacefully went to sleep. It now became clear to me what she meant. I had been airlifted to the burn unit the day before Bianca's first birthday. That, obviously, was when the music stopped and my face had been changed forever, leaving her with the subconscious image and memory.

I read these words to my now 25-year-old daughter, and she not only doesn't remember it, but thinks it's strange yet curious. I agree, however I know it happened. I was 26 years old when I became aware of my spiritual journey. We talked openly regarding her belief that life "just happens," which differs from my belief in God. I respect and admire the young woman that stands before me. I love that we respect each other without judgment. To me, that is what I had prayed for... being the best mother I could be, to love unconditionally, to lead by example, and be able to let go and allow my children to spread their wings and develop their own spiritual journey.

Sometime after going to the 12-step support group, I accepted an invitation to go out for coffee with a few of the men and women. Socializing was awkward at first. I found comfort in joining others who understood my challenges before going home to an empty house on the Friday nights Bill had our children.

Carlos was one of the men I had become friendly with. After almost two years of developing a friendship, Carlos would playfully say, "take a risk and kiss me."

I would reply, "You're too nice of a guy for my high-maintenance life with three young children." Nevertheless, he continued to remain my friend.

I began planning a New Year's Eve party to celebrate Y2K. My cousin Franca came to visit with her husband and one-year old son in December of 1999. Carlos joined the seven of us on a day trip to New York City. We shopped and enjoyed the sights of the Holidays.

We were back at Penn Station awaiting our train home when David, Franca's husband, vomited into a garbage pail! That was the beginning of a domino effect for all of us, with the exception of Carlos. Carlos graciously stayed at my house that night helping change and wash the kids' sheets. He also held my hair back for me while I knelt over the porcelain bowl! His kindness prompted me to consider slowly taking down some of the metaphoric walls I had put in place while my broken heart was mending.

I had been a single mom for over five years, while working on healing a lifetime of emotional wounds. It took me from December 1999 until December 2000 to finally "take the risk." On December 12, 2000, I kissed him.

To sum up the past 20 plus years, Carlos and I were married in December 2001. We blended our families; he raised two children who were young adults when we were married. I sold my home and moved in the summer of 2001 with my three children and our cats Lola and Mr. Cat. (Lola was one of Katie's kittens; Katie wasn't fond of being a young mother and ran off one day never to return. Mr. Cat showed up on our back deck shortly after Katie left, so he pretty much adopted us). Carlos was a maintenance manager at an estate before it became a charitable foundation. The estate's heiress hired him personally in 1981 at her residence in Newport, Rhode Island. A year later, she moved him and his family to one of the historic homes on her estate property in New Jersey.

After we were married, moving into that home was the most practical choice for us financially. Our home on the estate was surrounded by hundreds of acres. We had eight fireplaces in this historic yet newly renovated colonial farmhouse – in a town with an outstanding school district. It was like a fairy tale come true for me. We bought two ATVs for me and my children to explore and enjoy the grounds. We fished, hiked and rode our bikes behind the gates of a 2,400-acre estate. It was an adjustment for my children, leaving their friends and starting over in a new school. I enrolled them in sports activities before we moved in to get them socialized with other children their age. My life was busy doing what I enjoyed most.

I talked to Gayle and let her know I made a decision to no longer attend the Wednesday night women's group. She encouraged me to reconsider, but also let me know I would always be welcomed back. It was comforting to know my support group was there if I needed them.

After returning from work on our first wedding anniversary in 2002, I was greeted by my children full of enthusiasm. They led me to the basement. The basement was in the process of renovation to provide a family room for our children. When I reached the bottom of the stairs, I saw an adorable black Labrador puppy, and in my opinion, the best dog ever. We named him Harley. Carlos had gotten a Treeing Walker hound dog a few months before we were married, we named her Maggie May. My brother thought Maggie looked like a beagle on steroids. She was about 60 pounds, mostly white with black and brown spots and sporting a pink nose. Her tall thin stature made her a head-turner. Harley and Maggie soon became best friends. Sadly, Maggie May vanished from our lives after countless marathons of running after her as she went out to explore the world and meeting countless good Samaritans who brought her home after her adventure. One of them became a very dear friend. After months of searching for her, we choose to believe that she was taken in by a family who offered her a full and wonderful life.

Carlos and I, and my kids, went to Boston to meet up with his daughter, her boyfriend and his family. They joined us to attend a Boston-Pittsburgh baseball game. Due to excruciating pain in my eyes, I had to leave the stadium and go back to the hotel before the game ended. I placed cold washcloths over both eyes. The pain was so severe it caused my body to tremble. The next morning Carlos asked hotel management if they could recommend an eye doctor that would take an emergency. Dr. Steven Foster came highly recommended. I was given an appointment right away. After meeting, we learned he is a renowned cornea specialist. He removed the eyelashes that were causing my eye irritation then gave me special eye drops to relieve the swelling. He asked to see me again in a few weeks to reevaluate my corneas after the swelling had gone down. He is familiar with Stevens-Johnson syndrome. Carlos and I made a weekend vacation out of that next visit. We even brought our well-behaved one-year old black lab, Harley, with us to a dog-friendly hotel. At this visit I learned the damage to my cornea was increasing and working in the salon was contributing to the severe inflammation. The threat of losing my eyesight was our biggest concern. Dr. Foster told me about a surgery of replacing the mucous membrane behind my eyelids, and it would require a six-month recovery per eye, with a 50% success rate. That information made my next decision a no-brainer. After that visit I realized I could no longer work in the salon. It was heartbreaking for me to know the profession I loved couldn't love me back.

So, I began looking at alternatives to my profession. I took a computer class but was challenged by eye pain and blurred vision. Words on the screen never stayed in focus, so in the meantime, I started caring for a client's 3-month-old daughter. Becky worked as a teacher a few miles from our home on the estate. A few years later she had a son who I cared for as well. Carlos and I referred to those children as our "practice" grandchildren.

It was time for some family fun, so I planned a vacation for us and my three children. It was the best vacation ever – a seven-day Disney cruise! We all had such a wonderful time. Michael was chosen as the "pin collector" of the week, and we were all invited to have dinner with the captain. I enjoyed going to the spa, while Carlos played bingo, the kids were off having the time of their lives. It was such a wonderful experience. Bianca, at 15, wanted to go back the following year in lieu of having a big Sweet 16 party. A few weeks after I booked our second cruise vacation, Carlos received word from his employer that severance packages were going to be offered to the managers and most of the employees. There was a threat that staff members could lose their positions if they chose not to take it. We did our best to put it out of our thoughts and enjoy our trip. Bianca brought a friend, and one of our friends also joined us with her son who was Anthony's age.

Still not knowing the intentions of Carlos's employer, the New Year had arrived. Carlos and I drove to Rhode Island to celebrate New Year's Eve with his friends and family. We left Rhode Island at 10:00 AM on January 2, 2004 to visit Carlos's son in Vermont. There was a light snowfall when we started off, but by the time we hit New Hampshire, the snow was thick, and the roads became icy. I decided to recline my seat and I placed a stuffed animal that looked like a black lab puppy behind my neck. My son Michael had given this to me for Christmas. It was the perfect size to double as a neck pillow. I also draped myself with my long coat for extra warmth.

It couldn't have been more than a few minutes after I settled in for the long ride ahead, when I heard Carlos shout, "Hold on!!!!!" I pulled the hood of my coat over my face, then reached up and held on to the strap near the top of the window. I braced myself as the truck slid across the road. There was a loud roar and then a crash – our truck flipped over onto the driver's side! The sounds were a combination of screeching thunder and the hum of hovercraft. The truck went airborne over a guardrail, my seat belt tightened against my chest as it secured me for the ride of my life. With each rollover, I heard the sound box my son had chosen to insert into the paw of the stuffed dog that was tucked behind my neck, "I love you. I love you. I love you." The sound box spoke. We rolled over three times, then slid into a tree on my side, yet somehow when the truck stopped it was back on its four wheels. The windshield had shattered and there were sheets of broken glass covering my coat.

In those first moments, there was complete silence. It was surreal. I pulled my hood off my face and saw the snow gently falling out of the sky. I heard Carlos whisper, "Are you okay?"

I looked over at him to say, "Yes," and gasped. His face was dripping with a thick blanket of dark red blood, and then I noticed his left forearm was out of place. I remember telling myself to stay calm. Within a few minutes a man appeared at Carlos's door. Apparently, there had been an accident ahead of us and that was the reason Carlos braked. Upon braking, he lost control on the black ice. The man introduced himself as a paramedic. He looked into the truck to see if we were okay, then suggested I get Carlos' wedding ring off his finger before his hand started to swell.

Our Chevy Avalanche was packed full of Christmas gifts along with bags of tchotchkes I bought at the Christmas Tree Shoppe. I was able to shift the truck into park, turn it off and unlock the doors. I also held Carlos's head in my hands while assisting the rescue team in getting him out of the truck. The roof on my side of the truck had caved in when we hit the tree. I had reclined my seat which now put my head protectively behind the roll bar of the truck. I was physically unharmed. My coat shielded me from the broken glass, my seat belt held me in place, the stuffed dog doubled as a neck brace, so my head didn't get bounced around, and having my seat reclined saved me from decapitation. My daughter Bianca said I had an Angel with me. I wholeheartedly believe she was right.

With assistance, I made it up the hill and I looked back at the wreck of our truck. It was a miracle we survived the horrific scene. The trees had broken branches covered with all our belongings – it looked as if the Christmas Tree Shoppe exploded in the woods. I was asked to ride in the front seat of the ambulance, apparently, I fainted, and the next thing I remembered was waking up next to Carlos in the back of the ambulance, mumbling out all my drug allergies. Thank God all was well. The doctors who examined me said I probably fainted due to a quick drop in adrenaline.

Carlos had to be transported to a second hospital to have surgery on his arm, which left him with a few screws that remain in his forearm.

My stepson drove in from Vermont to drive us back home to New Jersey after Carlos was discharged. That was when **my** symptoms kicked in. I may have dodged physical injuries; however, the drive back home proved my emotions and nerves were badly fractured. I was so stressed out I had to sit in the back seat. Carlos and I came up with a name for my continuing "passenger-seat" disability; we call it "CARettes Syndrome" because I have no control over the noises or profanity that I call out when I'm a passenger in a car. I always apologize to whoever is driving before we travel. My doctor prescribed Xanax to help with anxiety. During long car rides, I keep the prescription with me for support, but of course I'm reluctant to digest any pills due to my history of reactions to meds. Just knowing I have it with me is usually sufficient.

As my skin was healing from the trauma of SJS back in 1989, my doctors had advised me to treat my skin as I would a baby's skin. I had written in the earlier chapters that I use sunscreen daily and I'm very vigilant in noticing any changes on my skin. In fact, I had noticed three separate clusters of freckles, as well as a slew of random freckles that showed up soon after I left the burn unit back in 1989. Before SJS, I had very few freckles on my extremities. Two of the three clusters were on my upper left thigh. One looked like a starburst, and the other in the shape of a horse's head. My eye has a wild imagination! The third cluster was on my upper left arm. This one looked like a Playboy bunny icon.

While on vacation in 2007 with Carlos and our friend and her husband, I noticed the cluster of freckles on my upper left arm changed. It no longer had the bunny head shape. By the week's end it had become darker in color, in spite of all the sunscreen I had been using. When we returned home, I scheduled to see my dermatologist. He was away so I saw his associate and had it biopsied. Soon after, I received a call from my dermatologist. The test was positive for stage 3 malignant melanoma (skin cancer). I was shocked, and my first (humorous) thought was that "the rabbit died, it was positive."

Upon receiving this diagnosis, I went to a Cancer Center. I had a three-inch margin of skin removed, requiring several stitches. When the biopsy came back, I was told the line of melanoma was distinguishable leaving me with a clean margin of cancer free tissue – and there would be no need for further treatment. It was such a relief to know it was self-contained. My doctor also informed me the most common metastasis of melanoma is Lung, Liver and Brain. In the early 2000's there were clinical trials for melanoma because it didn't respond to traditional cancer treatments. My doctor believed I wouldn't qualify for the clinical trials because my immune system was compromised due to having SJS/TEN. The day I had my first biopsy, a young mom from the town I moved from was in the waiting room awaiting the same procedure I had. Her results proved the melanoma had metastasized, sadly she passed away a few months after her diagnosis. I was so sad for her family; I knew I was very fortunate for my early diagnosis. I returned to the cancer institute for an examination each year over five years with no other signs of cancer.

In 2008, once again my mobile of life was thrown off balance when Carlos was told his position at the estate had been terminated. We were given 27 days to move out of the house that Carlos had called home for almost 26 years, and our home we had created over the past six years. Bianca was attending and living at Rutgers and Anthony had just passed his driving test. He and Michael were both in high school when this emotional hurricane rocked our world. Simultaneously, the bank I had invested my settlement money in had filed for bankruptcy, leaving me with a diminished savings account to rely on.

Challenged by the "Why me's," while standing on the edge of the pity pot of life's bitter soup, I cast the blame on the "charitable" foundation that caused us this pain. Thankfully, Carlos had been hired by a historical restoration company within a week of his termination, leaving me to pack up over 26 years of his collection of belongings, and six years of ours, in less than four weeks – while looking for an affordable home for our family.

Our friends and family were so helpful during those few weeks of packing up and cleaning out our home. On day 27, the house was empty and spotless, with only three boxes of washed and folded employee apparel on the floor in the barren parlor. Only three weeks prior, it was beautifully furnished with antiques, photographs and family heirlooms.

Standing numb with pure exhaustion, I watched as the new Foundation manager and his sidekick walked through the house for the final inspection.

One of Bianca's friends was there to take photographs of the house as proof of our efforts to leave it with dignity. Ariane's beautiful spirited energy was welcomed as a gift to me that day. I even cracked a smile after one of the men questioned her about her photo compositions, asking if she meant to take a photo of him. Her reply both honest and playful was, "No, but I will take your picture if you'd like me to."

As Carlos and I turned to give this beautiful house our final glance, one of the men extended his hand to Carlos. Carlos hesitated, then reluctantly extended his. That handshake sent an energy of a sucker punch to the gut, one that would take much time to heal.

We moved into my parents' house while awaiting to close on the house we had rushed to purchase.

Once again, I'm living in my childhood home. (None of which was written into my journal in 1990 when I prayed for an awesome life! God has some sense of humor.) Gratefully, my parents were accommodating and gracious.

[Coincidental Side Note: Today is November 29, 2013, and I'm sitting in Newark Airport while I'm typing away on my iPad mini. Carlos is in Vermont visiting his son, our daughter-in-law, and our first grandchild, who was born seven days ago. I'm on my way to visit my childhood friend, Sharon, for her 50th birthday celebration. I didn't realize how late it was until I was distracted by a pigeon walking past me while sitting at my original Gate A22. I looked at the time on my iPad only to realize my plane had already left the airport without me! OH MY GOODNESS! I was so deep into a writing zone, I didn't notice how much time had passed, nor that they had changed the gate. A compassionate customer service woman, after announcing my name THREE times for my flight, placed me on the next flight. Ironically, boarding time was 3:34, which was our house address on the Estate.]

So... where was I?

The challenges that inundated our lives due to the trauma of our situation tested my faith and challenged our marriage. I was so angry. I questioned God and why this was happening to my family. While spewing resentment in my journal, we made choices that created even more turmoil. We anxiously purchased a house that needed more work than we were prepared to do. Along with onerous turn of events with the

165

challenges of having two teenage boys, I remember saying, "I prayed for healthy babies, I didn't say anything about arrogant teenagers!" Parenting three teens took vigilance and energy. I was catapulted back to the days of little to no sleep.

Soon after we moved into my parents' house, I was hired as a school bus aide for special needs children. I enjoyed this fun little job that offered me great health benefits. After three years, I was sadly one of the first 26 employees to be let go when New Jersey education cutbacks took place. It seemed as if "the good, the bad, and the ugly" was off symmetry.

As if losing my job and health benefits wasn't enough, my eye pain had become unbearable. Bad and Ugly had bullied Good out of town.

Chapter Twenty
~ Fortitude ~

Glimmers of hope began to show up through the amazing staff and team of eye doctors at Paul Phillips Eye & Surgery Center in Flemington, NJ. I had been referred there in 2009 when my usual eye doctor was on vacation. My first visit came as an emergency. I was given an appointment promptly. Carlos was my driver because I was unable to keep my eyes open due to the pain of my inflamed corneas. I briefed Dr. Philips on my condition and told him my history including my visits to a cornea specialist in Boston. After treating me by removing the eyelashes that were causing me pain, he then offered me an open-door invitation, allowing me to be treated pro bono as often as needed. His kindness is such a blessing to me. Soon after, I learned that one of the doctors in his practice remembered meeting me while I was in the burn unit 20 years earlier. That doctor even recalled my room number. I've seen all the doctors in the practice due my frequent eyelash extraction visits. One of the doctors in the practice suggested I try a contact lens that would work as a band-aid to protect my cornea from the torment of lashes under my eyelids. I wasn't able to get the contact lenses in or out of my eyes at first. Carlos and my son Michael were so supportive as they helped me. Once I mastered it on my own, I felt as if I returned to some sense of normalcy. While the contacts are in my eyes, the agonizing pain is gone. With humbling gratitude to all the outstanding doctors and staff at Paul Phillips Eye & Surgery Center, my faith began to be restored.

Hope and faith are what jump-started my failing will as I pushed through the challenges before me. I pulled myself out of the victim pool and into a cleansing sea to remove the bad and ugly from my life.

Parenting teenagers to adulthood took on an adventure of obstacles. I put on my invisible Superhero cape and went up against teenage challenges. Utilizing the wisdom of my experiences, while embracing my mission to be a good parent with Carlos' support, we conquered the demons that attempted to charm my children. Setting boundaries and following through was the most difficult for me, knowing respect, self-value and self-discipline are the greatest gifts we can offer our children. The reality is we all need to practice discipline, whether it be with food, shopping, alcohol, social media – the list is endless. As a parent, I can only hope all our effort has been received. Maybe someday when I reread my journals from that time in my life, I'll find some humor in the "Mom turns mad dog" stories. After my youngest son Michael's 20th birthday, I wanted to have a shirt made for myself with the words, "**I survived 3 teenagers!**"

In June 2012, I had the two children I took care of when I lived on the estate visit for the day. It was their Mom's last day of teaching for the school year. After a day at my sister's pool, we went back to my house. Nine-year-old Becca and I were sitting on a hammock when the hook it hung from snapped. My butt hit the pavers with the weight of Becca on me. I was so glad she didn't get hurt, however, the pain that followed after the shock of the fall was excruciating. I had to lay flat for three weeks while a fracture to my sacral bone healed (So basically, I broke my butt!). Being unable to perform daily activities, I stayed at my parents' house with my dog Harley and our newest little dog Min for the first few days.

One bittersweet memory I have is ... laying on a wicker couch on my parents' beautiful enclosed deck, enjoying the sounds of the songbird my Mom graciously keep well fed. (My mom had been diagnosed with dementia several years before, causing short term memory loss). She had asked me if I would like a glass of water. It was a warm day, so I welcomed it. When she returned, she had a plate of watermelon, and asked me again if I would like a glass of water. This pattern repeated until the table in front of me was filled with various food choices. I couldn't help but laugh with my mom when I brought it to her attention; she had set out to bring me only a glass of water, and in its place was a table full of food. She then walked back into the house chanting, "water, water, water," returning with a glass of water while still repeating her chant as she handed it to me. We both laughed so hard it brought tears to my eyes. The stabbing pain that followed from laughing was well worth it. A sense of humor truly helps us get through our most difficult and sad challenges.

The summer of 2012 had a series of ups and downs. For example, there was another car accident that could have been tragic but thankfully ended with a totaled car and no serious injuries. On the upside, my cousin Franca visited from

Venezuela to surprise my dad for his 80th birthday party celebration.

That same summer, after having an MRI, my orthopedic doctor sent results to my gynecologist that indicated a large cyst on my left ovary that had to be removed at once. Our health insurance through Carlos' work cost over $1,100 per month with a $5,000 deductible for each of us. We were already living paycheck to paycheck prior to the hammock malfunction. This was the first time in my life I had financial debt. I was never one to spend what I didn't have; however, the medical bills were unavoidable. It was a new emotional low for me, crying out in my journal, "Enough! Why the f%$# is this happening to ME?"

In mid-August my friend Sharon had driven to New Jersey from Florida with her son to get him settled into college. She was with me the day my doctor called with the news of finding the cyst on my ovary. Her presence was so supportive. She prayed with me and reminded me how faith will return balance to the emotional storm I was experiencing. I was so happy to be reminded of that truth. I purged my anger and my gratitude while writing in my journal, I cried with both physical and emotional pain throughout that summer.

Have you ever met someone for the first time and felt as if you knew them your entire life? That was how I felt when I met Sherry DePinto back in 2004. Both of my sons played on the same pop warner football team as her son Michael.

Our two Michaels were like two peas in a pod, they define their friendship as kindred spirits.

Sherry was so excited to tell me about a group she was planning to attend to get support with personal challenges that surrounded her son, Michael. She met a woman at a conference who shared the name of an expert counselor for addiction and family counseling. It was Gayle Potter! I couldn't help but laugh out loud! "Yes, Virginia, there is a Santa Claus!" Immediately, I felt a sense of serenity embrace me, filling myself with the truth that we are never alone, and always guided. Sherry refers to these times as "GOD-incidences."

After almost ten years, I returned to the Wednesday night women's group facilitated by Gayle. Humbly, my heart was no longer broken, however my butt and wallet were. I was welcomed by both new and familiar faces. After a brief update, Gayle told me about a radio station that aired a financial talk show. I tuned in the next day, downloaded his book, and attended the workshop it offers with Carlos. I'm grateful and happy to announce I am months away from being debt-free of my medical bills.

Confident with the comfort of my contact lenses, accompanied by my glasses for vison correction, I consulted with my eye doctor regarding going back to work in the hair salon. I wanted to try to go back to work part-time. Being a hairstylist has always been a passion of mine. It's true that if you love what you do, you never work a day in your life. I called my former boss Anthony and asked him I if could work at the salon on Sundays and Mondays. The salon was usually closed on those days so there wouldn't be the threat of hair spray and chemicals used by other stylists. He graciously gave me the key to the salon and offered me the opportunity to make my own hours. In less than two years, I had a following of loyal clients who I can confidently call my friends. One in particular has been instrumental in getting this book finished and edited; Susan is such a special and supportive friend. She continued to encourage me to keep writing. She would cheer me on when my self-destructive low self-esteem 'head talk' would grab a hold of me. I chose to listen to my intelligent friend, instead of the self-sabotaging that once ran my life. I will forever be thankful for her confidence in me, as well as grateful for her walking into the salon and sitting in my chair to have her hair done.

Challenges and blessings continue to ebb and flow in my life. Writing this book has been an unexpected, yet welcomed, healing experience for me. I began writing to bring awareness to SJS/TEN, by sharing my story; however, I could have never imagined how writing this book would transform and catapult my OWN spiritual awareness to a deeper level.

I've come to realize how writing in my journal not only deepened my spiritual journey, but also provided me with a better understanding of why I have made some unfavorable choices as well as favorable ones. I utilized paper and pen to purge my pain, my feelings, my emotions, and most importantly, my gratitude. I now have a better understanding of the meaning of codependency, much like addiction, it could be a family disease deeply rooted in a lifetime of suppressing painful memories and potentially predisposing one to misuse or excessively use e.g. alcohol, work, people, drugs, food, exercise, sex, gambling, hoarding... the list is endless. All of which are utilized to suppress feelings. Keeping **too** busy has been one of my codependent challenges. I "came to believe" being chronically late is my biggest character defect. I continue to do my best to stay vigilant to how awful I feel about myself when I make my friends and family have to wait for me. I've taken notice that it happens most when I'm not taking care of myself. It's a daily struggle for me. A mantra I remind myself of is "I hope to notice it sooner and change it faster."

God knows that over the past 24 years, I had countless doctors offer me medications for physical and emotional pain. I guess the fear of taking pills has worked in my favor.

To those who have been affected with the disease of addiction, there is no making light of the disease, it's a lifetime healing process. I've witnessed addiction enter into the smallest crevices of a soul, using its poison to destroy lives and families.

Your soul can heal!

Comparative to cancer, without utilizing treatment, it has a very low life expectancy. However, the disease of addiction does not have written prescriptions for a pharmacist to fill. Only the affected person can write and fill their prescription.

The treatment plan starts with **choice.** Choosing to live your best life, choosing to ask for help, choosing to grieve, choosing to forgive, starting with forgiving yourself. Healing from the inside out.

Some antidotes with success rates are a commitment to:
- Professional treatment
- 12 Step groups
- Religious organizations
- Spiritual journey of your understanding
- Faith

Faith provides me a true sense of peace and joy, far greater than the temporary relief substance/compulsive behavior offers. Denial of such behavior may create the illusion of taking away the pain for a while, however, it ultimately causes more bondage to the pain...regardless if it's physical or emotional pain. A lifetime commitment, progress not perfection. In my life experience, I've come to notice, sobriety* breeds clarity and serenity.
(*Sobriety: the quality of being staid or solemn)

Note: I do take medication when it's appropriate and necessary, such as the medication prescribed for neuropathy due to pain and numbness in both my hands and feet. It has become increasingly painful. (Neuropathy is common in SJS/TEN survivors due to the damage of the nerve endings in their skin).

Chapter Twenty-One
~ Coincidences ~

Several months into writing this book, I came across an SJS survivor's story on the SJS website using photos and captions while a song played in the background. This inspired me to write in my journal how I too would like to share my own personal timeline of photos to a special song.

Life's coincidences never cease to amaze me. One that can't go unmentioned is meeting Brandon, formerly a member of the band, *Pilot for a Day,* at the salon I worked at in 2013. Brandon was preparing to go on tour with his band. He came into the salon for a haircut. Brandon didn't have an appointment, so I extended my schedule and he returned at the end of my workday with his lovely young wife. Prior to leaving the salon, Brandon gifted me with a CD from his band. I began listening to it on my ride home from work. The first two songs were really good. Once I was halfway through, listening to the lyrics of the third song, "Extraordinary Life," I felt as if it were speaking directly to my spirit. There was no doubt this was the gift I had asked for, and no song could have been more perfect.

Music and Lyrics by: PILOT FOR A DAY

SONG: Extraordinary Life
(Featured Andrew Volpe)
(A few lines from some of the verses read)

This extraordinary life
It's all around you

As you blur into the scenery

And when your walls come crashing
to the ground
I'll be there waiting

Do you fight for every minute
While the time just slips on by

Rise up Rise up
Or this life will pass you by

As one of my clients said, "Coincidental miracles happen."

My 50th birthday was approaching, and I was more than halfway through writing my memoir when I sent a Facebook message to Brandon regarding my interest in using the song for my timeline of photos.

Late morning on the day of my 50th birthday as I sat in the waiting room of my dermatologist office, my phone rang while simultaneously my name was called by the medical technician. I silenced the call as it went to voicemail. I was so looking forward to this appointment, to not only have a concerning lump near the scar on my left arm checked out (it was next to the scar where the stage 3 melanoma skin cancer had been removed in 2006), but to jokingly remind my doctor of his pep talks 24 years prior. When he would reassure my damaged skin would only be 25 years old when

I'm 50 years old". I was having my one-year full body scan, so it was routine to get undressed and into a paper gown. After my doctor of 24 years greeted me with a hug, I then pointed to my face as if to draw an imaginary circle around it and stated, "This is not looking 25!"

He chuckled and said, "You always looked pretty Alicia, and you look wonderful at 50!"

He proceeded to tell me about his awful divorce that took place over the past year, then he gave me an all clear after the examination and recommended I make an appointment for my one year follow up upon leaving.

While on my drive home, I realized he didn't mention anything regarding the lump near the scar on my left arm above my elbow; it had become sensitive to the touch and concerning for me.

Once I returned home, I called the office back and explained my situation. The receptionist recommended I call the cancer institute and follow up there. I did just that. The receptionist at the cancer institute told me since it has been more than 5 years, I needed to see my dermatologist. "UHGGGG"... so I called the dermatologist office again and made an appointment for the following week.

Home in my living room, I retrieved the voicemail left on my phone. I was so happy to hear it was a message from Brandon. Unbeknownst to him, he called on my birthday. His voice was filled with such conviction and compassion, exactly matching my emotions. He explained how he struggled with writing just the right reply to my request. He wanted to let me know, in just the right way, that he would be honored to let me use the song for such a personal and important message. The events of my day concluded with a surprise birthday party, celebrating with my family and friends.

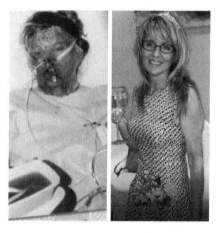

Alicia 26 years old 1989 ~ Alicia's 50th Birthday 2014

One week after my birthday, I returned to my dermatologist to show him the lump on my upper left arm. After he looked it over, he reassured me the lump was no more than a LIPOMA. He explained that a lipoma was a non-threatening small cluster of tissue. Phew…. that was such a relief.

Early that fall I drove to our families Upstate New York vacation home with my dad and my two dogs Harley and Min. I boxed up my Journals dated 1989 through 2009 with the exception of the one I wrote while I was in the burn unit. And a few I'd like to reread someday.

Those drives to NY State with my dad over the past 40 years are some of the best conversations of my life. He is such a good storyteller. He shared stories about his life, his friends and when he was in the army. He is so proud of his 'Rutgers family' and shares his accomplishments as a learning tool to always follow your dreams.

My parents are the most loving generous couple I know. I use the word couple because that is who they are. My parents met when my dad was 18 years old. He was out at a swimming lake with some friends shortly before joining the army at the time of the Korean War. My mom was 16 years old. She was walking past the lake to the local town bakery to pick up a birthday cake for her baby cousin Yvonne. The rest is their story. My dad loves my mother so deeply; she will forever be his sweetheart. After over 60 years of marriage, he still referred to my mom as his bride, and the baby cousin, Yvonne, is still his flower girl. My dad's beautiful heart has a way to allow everyone he meets feel special, especially his friends and family.

This time the almost four-hour car ride with a stop at the diner was the perfect time to read my book to him. After each chapter we had a chat session discussing it. He looked at me with pride in his eyes. I asked him if he would help me to get a fire going in the fire pit once we were settled in from the ride.

I had retrieved all the information necessary to complete this book and was ready to let go, peeling back another layer of that metaphorical onion. I brought my journals to burn them as a symbolic healing.

We had the campfire started before dark. I sat with myself and over two decades of this beautiful journey we call life. I cried tears of sadness and tears of joy while glancing to read a paragraph or two before tossing the pages into the fire. Joy trumped sadness while gratitude and faith won over fear.

I continue to thank God and my heavenly and earthly Angels for all the love and blessings in my life. Remembering the gifts, I received while my body and flesh were under attack:

"You will live for the son."
"They have their own."
"It's time to heal."

Chapter Twenty-Two
~ A Note to My Readers ~

My intention was to end my story at chapter 21 and have it published soon after. Due to unexpected life changes my story stayed in my computer for the next five years.

To summarize the past 5 years, with a poetic twist...six months after my 50th birthday, I went back to the dermatologist because the lump on my left arm had increased in size and became tender to the touch. This time it proved to be stage 3 metastatic melanoma cancer. After two surgeries, damage to my Thoracic 1 & 2 nerves painfully affecting the use of my left arm, a collapsed lung, and an allergic skin reaction due to being given Tylenol with Codeine (an oversight of my medication chart), the cancer had spread to my left lung. A biopsy confirmed the diagnosis was stage 4 metastatic melanoma lung cancer with less than a year life expectancy....

Cancer
Blessing or Curse

It came as a curse
dark thoughts in my head

Sadness and fear of dying
Stomped on my faith

Self-loathing snuck in
Tears of pity entered my soul

Threats of death told again and again
Wheeling calendar dates consumed my thoughts

Time slowed to a stop while speeding ahead
Obsessive worry, will I survive,
a year or just a month till I'm dead?

Treatment plan is launched
Eerily quiet it began to flow

Preparing for what is to be expected
Crashing waves of torment captured my body

Overwhelming support spread worldwide
Lifted up my spirit as if being carried

All the prayers, love and well wishes
settle into my soul
Renewing my faith while keeping me whole

Life comes to a screeching halt!
Holding my breath... as if there is no air
My doctor reveals your scans are "all clear"

Shock shows up first
Then tears of Joy

Not long after, questions arise
Sorrow in knowing so many have died
Remorsefully pondering why did I survive

Warriors like me placed into my life
Kindred spirits sharing our fight

Celebrating those who arduously kept me alive
Knowing they strive for more to survive

We join together heroically
Standing side by side

There are no coincidences
of that I am sure

Blessings appear
Let them in and discover...
The Miracle is you

… It seems God had other plans for me, I'm going on 5
years and counting – CANCER FREE!

~ Christmas 2019 ~

Alicia, (dog) Mini
Eugene, Anthony, Elena, Bianca, Michael, Aleks

Epilogue
~ Remember ~

When I finished writing chapter eleven, I asked my mom if she would like me to read it to her.

She replied, "No. I lived it. I don't need to read about it!"

I told her that Chapter Eleven was about Michael's birth.

She angrily replied, "I hope you didn't write about the things Bill did or said!"

"Mom, this is my memoir, I'm writing what I can remember and what I wrote in my journal."

She said, "Alicia, you have to forget that! You have to put it out of your mind!"

I sat silently in her kitchen until my spirit found its voice. "I'm remembering and writing because it's healing for me. I deserve to heal. If I chose to forget all the bad, or sad things that I have experienced, I may lose control over what I forget."

She looked at me. "Yes," she said, "You should keep writing."

Our conversation took place on July 28, 2013, a few months after I started writing my story.

I was staying overnight with my two awesome dogs, Harley (my ten-year-old black Lab) and Mini (my seven-year-old Yorkie\ Jack Russell mix). My dad had gone to up-state New York with my nephew that weekend to our family vacation home. My mom no longer tolerated the four-hour car ride, so she hadn't been there in a few years, I was spending the weekend to keep her company.

That night when I went to bed in the bedroom I had as a teenager, and the same room I was in before going to the hospital in September 1989, I pondered the conversation that corresponded between my mom and me. I began to wonder if there could be a correlation between believing you must forget the pain, and dementia.

How different would my mom's life have been if she was told she could heal her pain? Instead of "forgetting it and putting it out of her mind."

It reminded me of the message I reserved through the dream I had while in the burn unit, "It's time to heal the women in our family."

I may not be able to heal my mom; however, I can choose to change the dynamic of that destructive false belief for myself and future generations of the women in my family.

I was gifted a book from my second cousin, Kelly, in 1996; its title is, *It's Never Too Late to Have A Happy Childhood* by Claudia Black. Two of her quotes that came to my mind while I was writing are...

1: "To free yourself from the past, you must break the rules of silence and compliance"

2: "Forgiving is not Forgetting, it is Remembering and letting go."

I pray for my mom; I know she has her own journey and I will do my best to honor her while accepting the challenges that are out of my control.

We all have a story. I invite you to write your story, then write about your present life and your future as if your past has been healed. We can heal together.

Epilogue
~ Part Two ~

My life journey has been a head shaker…

I couldn't find the words to describe the thoughts that went through my mind when I was first diagnosed with a life-threatening cancer at the end of 2014. Unbeknownst to Bianca, Eugene was preparing to ask her hand in marriage. It seemed inconceivable to miss out on that milestone of her life.

I had an urgency to start a bucket list including a "face-my-fear list. Self-publishing this book is on the top of both those lists.

My friend Donna, aka Minnie Mouse from chapter five, planned a girl's weekend after I started treatment in January 2015. I was told at best there was less than a 10% chance of the cancer not spreading. Donna, Robin, Linda, Sherry and I laughed, cooked, drank, ate and played games like a bunch of schoolgirls in that beautiful vacation resort house. I even had a fireplace in my bedroom. Saturday morning, I woke to the smell of fresh coffee brewing and the sight of at least eight inches of snow on the wraparound deck that shared an entrance from my designated bedroom. I put on my boots and jacket before going out on the deck. Large fluffy snowflakes continued to float from the sky. I remember falling to my knees while I sobbed with the thought of this being the last snowfall I would see before I died. One by one my friends sat in the snow with me as they cradled me in a rocking group hug. We cried until our tears turned into laughter with the thought of five grown woman covered in snow impersonating a giant snowball. I felt their love to the depth of my soul that weekend.

Sadly our, beautiful 12-year-old Black Lab, Harley became ill, I took him to vet, he was diagnosed with Lung Cancer. (FYI - we are a **non**-smoking family.) Harley passed away a few weeks before I was told I was in remission.

After Bianca and Eugene's engagement, my dad and I went to Italy to visit our cousins in Sicily in the summer of 2015. I was fifteen years old the last time I was there with my dad and my beloved grandpa Bianco. It was wonderful to check that off my bucket list. However, I would like to visit again with my children someday.

Between the years 2015 through 2019, we celebrated Bianca and Eugene's wedding, my boys graduated from college, my son Michael and his girlfriend Aleks celebrated their engagement (with a wedding to follow in 2021), our grandson Max became a big brother with the arrival of Weston and both boys became cousins with the birth of my beautiful granddaughter Elena Rose (the best way to describe being a Grammy is PURE JOY!).

Seven weeks after Elena was born my beloved dad passed away. I know he is smiling and watching over us. His presence in my heart comforts me.

In Chapter Nineteen, I mentioned that our circumstances began to challenge our marriage, ultimately leaving me to peel away another layer of the metaphoric onion. At the end of 2017, I took the arduous leap (of fear) to move out on my own for the first time in my life. I am embracing this new chapter of my life.

In conclusion, a quote I've read countless times:

Quoted by: Nelson Mandela

Our deepest fear is not that we are inadequate
Our deepest fear is that we are powerful beyond measure
It is our light not our darkness that most frightens us
We ask ourselves," Who am I to be brilliant, gorgeous, talented and fabulous?'

Actually, who are you not to be?
You are a child of God.

Your playing small doesn't serve the world.

There's nothing enlightening about shrinking so that other people won't feel insecure around you.

We were born to manifest the glory of God that is within us.
It's not just in some of us; it's in everyone.

As we let our own light shine, we unconsciously give others the permission to do the same.

As we liberate from our own fear, our presence automatically liberates others.

Written by Marianne Williamson

Paying it forward.

With much love,
Alicia

~ YouTube of Timeline coming soon ~

~ Acknowledgments ~

Coincidental miracles happen. Or are they 'God-incidents'? Simultaneously, I became surrounded with unconditional guidance and support in bringing this book to fruition.

Starting with Gayle Potter, Veronica Serino and all the women in our Wednesday night women's group throughout the past 25 years. Thank you all for parenting me into adulthood.

To the numerous clients and co-workers from Anthony Vincent Salon naming just a few; Anthony Vincent, Alyse Tapper, Mara Tapper , Raymond Simpkins, (Susan Mullica did my first edit; this book is legible because of you), Lissa Gjertsen, Barbara-Hopkins Kelly, Catherine (Cat) , Barb Harrington, Anne White, Eileen Lavadera, Brandon Rimmy, Renee Sachs and Carol Rickard who restarted my passion to have this book published. Carol you are one of my many earth Angels.

To all of my aunts, uncles, cousins, family and friends that have been mentioned in my life journey. I love you with all my heart.

To my siblings Gina, Angela and Joe along with my brother in-laws Ken and Ray and sister-in-law, Sylvia. Thank you for your continued love and support.

My dear sister friend, Karen Garland and her family, your friendship is immeasurable.

Gratitude goes out to Carlos for being there while I was getting to know me. Thank you for sharing your beautiful family with me. Especially our grandsons Maxwell and Weston!

To name just a few of the inspiring ladies in my life, Yvonne Walsh, Kelly, Jen, Franca Bianco, Donna Genito, Sharon, Robin Scarpatti, Sherry DePinto, Karen Bodoh, Ann Bastian, Symantha Erme, Karen Doyle Rodgers, Linda, Kathy Platt, Kathryn Weidener, Patrice Faraone, Mary Jane Pierce, Lori Kelty, Hilary and Amy, Thank you for being you!

Becky, Becca, Ryan and Brian Edgerly. Brian your talent amazes me. Thank you for creating my vision for the book cover.

To the children in my heart: Eugene, Aleks, Stacy, Jason, Zac, Kim, the Lemeire family, Julius Muhirwe, along with all of Bianca, Anthony and Michael's friends. I've been blessed with all of you.

Love to my nieces and nephews.

The most incredible blessing to date was the gift given to me by my daughter Bianca and son in law Eugene. Watching my granddaughter come into this world will forever be embedded in my heart. Elena Rose arrived just in time to be held by her Great Grandpa Joe. Her sweet spirit provides immeasurable comfort surrounding the passing of my beloved Dad.

Continuing thanks and gratitude to Dr. Paul Phillips and his amazing staff at **Paul Phillips Eye & Surgery Center**. Your kindness and wholehearted care for my eye health continues to improve my quality of life.

To Dr. Elizabeth Phillips for your dedication to the research of SJS/TEN, and for your contributions to this book.

And to God and my Angels, for all the love and blessings in my life.

~ Shared Memories ~

Karen Garland:

Once in a lifetime someone comes into your life and you think "this should be my sister!" That is how I feel about Alicia. We can spend a day together and cry one minute and the next laugh so hard that tears run down your leg. She is the friend I hope never to be without. We have been through so many things together, deaths and births and all the in-between things. Nothing could have prepared me for the events that happened 24 years ago.

Alicia called me and said she wasn't feeling good, could I come over to her house and get her young daughter so she could rest. I picked up Bianca and told Alicia to call me when she wanted her home. I told her she should call the doctor because she looked even worse. I didn't hear from her the next day, which was so unlike her, so I called her sister Gina who told me Alicia was in the hospital. Gina said she was REALLY SICK! Then Gina called me to say they were taking her to a burn center. I couldn't believe this was happening to the kindest and sweetest person I knew.

Each day Gina or her other sister Angela would call with a report and each day I was afraid I would never see Alicia again. I remember a call where they said she got her period. I thought that was such a weird thing to be happy to report. I later learned it meant that her female organs were working.

While Alicia was in the burn center, her baby Bianca took her first steps while being cared for by her paternal grandmother. I remember they agonized over whether to tell Alicia. They weren't sure if she would be upset that it happened while she was in the hospital or if she would take joy in the fact that her daughter was flourishing without her. They did tell her and of course Alicia was overjoyed that Bianca was walking but very sad she wasn't there to witness it.

I drove her two sisters crazy telling them at first that I wanted to see Alicia then I told them I needed to see her. They told me how bad she looked and that if I wanted to see her, I had to prepare myself. They said I could not get upset because that would only upset Alicia. I didn't care how bad she looked, I missed my friend and I didn't want her to feel she was going through this alone. The drive up to the hospital seemed like an eternity, and I was nervous that I would not be able to hold it together.

When I got to the hospital Alicia was in a visitors' lounge, I was overjoyed to see my friend. But all the prayers could not help me. I felt my legs go weak and my heart break when I saw this beautiful young woman before me; she looked like she was wearing a scary Halloween mask. I took a long deep breath and nervously talked about my kids and the weather or anything that came into my head. All I kept thinking was "Dear God how did this happen to my friend!" She told me a little about what happened to her, but she talked so low it was hard to hear her. Either that or I just couldn't wrap my mind around all the horror she had been through. It was my only visit to the hospital; I couldn't wait for her to get out of there and for her to be better and to be reunited with her beloved daughter.

I thank God every night that Alicia survived SJS/TEN and that thanks to many doctors, she is as beautiful now as she was before she got sick!

Franca Bianco:

Alicia never stopped, but she was so ill with a high fever; I thought she had the measles. My sister and I were helping out by taking care of her baby Bianca. I was with her when she was shaking in the bathtub with cold water... she wanted to get better for her daughter.

Lori Kelty:

I returned to work part time night shift after the birth of my first child, a daughter. About a year later, while working 11p-7a in the ICU, I was assigned to care for a young woman who had a severe allergic reaction to a derivative of penicillin. She was in critical condition and had developed SJS. With almost ten years of ICU/ED/Trauma experience, I had learned about this reaction but never actually treated anyone with this rare condition. At first glance, I saw a beautiful, petite, young girl resting with her eyes closed, realizing she was heavily sedated and very sick. As I looked closer, I noticed her sheets were wet. Then I discovered the blisters. All over her body were large pink/red fluid filled blisters. As they ruptured, her skin sloughed, and the fluid ran down her body to the sheets below. Treatment of SJS is similar to burns. The goals are to eliminate the trigger, while maintaining blood pressure, fluid volume and temperature. Caring for this young lady was challenging. Every time the blood pressure cuff inflated, blisters would rupture, draining fluid to the sheets below. Despite using warming blankets, the wet sheets would cool quickly, making temperature control impossible. I had to change her sheets frequently but turning her was difficult because any contact with her skin just caused more damage. The plastic electrodes used to monitor her heart refused to adhere to her wet skin and had to be replaced constantly. IV fluids pouring into several sites were secured only by gauze dressings because tape would not stick. As her arms swelled, the IV catheters would move out of the vein and new sites had to be established. Throughout the night, we worked on her constantly, praying she would survive until a burn center could accept the transfer. I was determined to keep her alive because she was so young and also had a baby daughter waiting for her at home.

After that night, I inquired about her several times, but no one had any updates on her condition. I thought about her often over the next couple of years but never heard anything about her outcome. Then fast forward to my daughter's orientation at Nursery School two years later. As our daughters explored the room, I started talking to one of the other young moms. She kept dabbing her wet eyes with a tissue and I thought she was crying. She explained how her tear ducts had been damaged after suffering a severe allergic reaction known as SJS. It wasn't too long after asking a few more questions, I realized she was my patient. That afternoon, she shared the rest of her recovery with me and we became good friends. Over the next several years, we each had two more children, hung together frequently and swapped childcare and carpool chores. After she moved away, I stalked her on social media and a few times actually ran into her at events. Alicia never realized how positively she impacted my life as a nurse, a mom and a friend.

Donna Genito:

It was like it happened on television, or in the news. My friend became sick from a mix of medicine, something any of us could have experienced. My sister Debby, who worked at the hospital, told me the horrific news that Alicia was burning from the inside out.

She described to me how Alicia looked and how she could not allow even a bed sheet to touch her skin because it would stick to her body. She said the helicopter would soon be there to transport her to the burn unit. This was all too surreal.

It was days before I could get there. My sister Debby and I drove to see Alicia. I had no idea what I would walk into. I was anxious to see my friend, who endured so much pain and suffering. What would she look like? How did she feel? Could she talk to me? Will she see or hear me? When I walked into her hospital room I was shocked. She was lying in bed, her entire body wrapped with gauze. She could speak to me; she whispered, "I miss my Dolly. I just want to go home and hold her."

My visit with Alicia was bittersweet. I was so happy to see her alive. I was relieved to know that she had such the will to fight and live. I knew in my heart she would get through this. I was shocked that this had happened, as many of us could not believe what Alicia had gone through.

There was always the smell of fine Italian food at the Bianco's and Alicia's grandmother made delicious soup! We sat at the dining room table trying to enjoy the food without acknowledging the difficulties Alicia had eating because of the tenderness she had in her mouth and throat.

A few months later, we spent the day just talking while the kids played. Alicia shared with me the deep scars in her heart, the things she heard while lying in the hospital and the pain she would never forget. We talked about planning a party for Bianca Rose.

In September 1990, she had a beautiful outdoor birthday party with friends and family in celebration of Bianca's 2nd birthday and Alicia's one-year anniversary of survival. I rented a costume and dressed up as Minnie Mouse. I sat inside the doorway of the play house in Alicia's parents back yard and took a photograph with each child at the party. I could see the joy in my girlfriend's eyes as I played the part of Minnie Mouse dancing with the children and sharing this very special day. It was truly a great celebration!

When I re-entered the party as Donna, no longer dressed as the character, a helicopter hovered overhead. I shouted, "Look everyone! Say goodbye to Minnie Mouse." The kids and the parents alike looked up in the sky and began waving to the Disney character. Alicia didn't say anything that day. It was years later before I knew how that helicopter flying by had triggered so much terror for her.

My girlfriend is truly an angel; I believe her life is a miracle.

Here we are thirty years later and most people have never heard of Stevens-Johnson Syndrome (SJS). I am so proud that my friend can share this painful life experience with the world today.

She is a blessing to everyone who shares her life. I love her with all my heart.

Patrice Faraone:

Shared her memory of that day with me. Patrice wrote: My perspective. I remember driving to hospital with your parents. I was so nervous as they kept stressing, don't say she looks good, and don't say she looks bad. Then, they were the 1st words out of my mouth!! From nerves. I was heartbroken for what you were going through, as we had children the same age and you were in this burn center unit. Holding on and fighting for dear life for the sake of Bianca. You telling me to "shut up" was such a normal reaction. It brought some levity to an awful situation. Your strength and determination to survive this unspeakable tragedy was amazing. I just got chills thinking about it.

Mary Jane:

As I try to recall the past (which is getting more and more difficult), there are some things I will never forget. Alicia and I had not been friends for long, but I knew when I met her that she was very special, full of love and kindness, a good wife and an adoring mother to baby Bianca Rose. When she was helicoptered to the Burn Center, I was so scared for her. I remember I went to see her a few times and prayed (seriously prayed) to God to help her. Slowly and through multiple procedures, she got better. But never all better. She was plagued with skin issues and eye problems for years. She always smiled though, always. She missed Bianca's first steps locked up in that burn unit. I don't know how she did it, although I'm sure the tears came when no one was around.

I was lucky enough to watch her have two more beautiful children, Anthony and Michael.

She helped me when I needed help during a difficult time in my life and will never forget it.

We remained friends; I would say close friends for years as our chapters ended and new ones began. Somehow, we have not spoken often in the past several years. She has been over more treacherous bridges.

Gina Bagala:

Many years later after my sister Alicia had been sick with Stevens-Johnson Syndrome, a very good friend's daughter, Jen, had become an ER nurse in Maryland. Jen shared that while she was working one night, a boy about 15 years old came into the ER very sick with big blisters covering his entire body (Jen was only 15 herself when Alicia suffered from SJS). The doctors were baffled. Jen said to the ER physician that when she was younger a friend of the family had gotten SJS and she remembered seeing photos that had looked similar to the teenager. They immediately ran blood work and discovered that the prognosis was indeed Stevens-Johnson Syndrome. The doctor turned to Jen and said, "You may have just saved this boy's life." Early recognition of SJS is especially important to reduce fatal outcomes. The boy was quickly transferred to a burn care unit where he was successfully treated.

Sherry DePinto:

Yes, meeting Alicia and her sweet Lab, Harley, loyally glued to her side, in the summer of 2004 was, without a doubt, a "God-incident." I know in my heart that we were purposefully placed in each other's lives to learn and experience together not so much simple life lessons (although we do that as well), but rather, lessons on a spiritual level. I feel like I have known her all my life. The best way to describe our friendship is "soul sisters."

Alicia has a gift and an extraordinary capacity to love. This is especially evident with children. She is a true live "Mary Poppins." Children, especially her beautiful grandchildren, energize her already brilliant light.

Although I didn't know her at the time she was inflicted with Stevens-Johnson Syndrome, I do witness the continued physical challenges it has left in its wake. Her eyes tear often, especially around irritants and she has to wear contact lenses to act as a barrier to the eyelashes that grow into her eyes. I still cringe at the thought of her doctor extracting those lashes without any anesthesia. But, Alicia doesn't let any of it bring her down; she does what she needs to do to take care of herself.

Alicia has been one of the greatest teachers in my life. In spite of the many earth-shaking challenges that Alicia has endured, I watch her dig deep and manage to keep believing. And, every time, miraculously, there is a rainbow at the end of every storm. It's as if God has used Alicia to be his messenger to reinforce the power of Faith in my own life. I am blessed and grateful for my beautiful friend.

Now Alicia has new purposes. Not only to bring awareness to SJS/TEN, she is meant to share her journey with the world and be that messenger of hope, gratitude, love and most importantly trust. Trust that even in the darkest times, persistence, support from others and Faith will get you through.

~ Book Commentary ~
by Elizabeth J. Phillips, MD

I.

"The Miracle of Me – A Memoir based on surviving and living with Stevens-Johnson syndrome and TEN" by Alicia Bianco is a graphic and honest account of one women's journey through life following Stevens-Johnson syndrome and toxic epidermal necrolysis (SJS/TEN). Alicia experienced SJS/TEN at age 26, only a few months after the birth of her first child. Now more than 30 years later, Alicia's vivid revision of her struggles, perseverance and long-term effects are an inspiration to all readers and particularly those who have personally experienced SJS/TEN, or have had family members who have survived or succumbed to SJS and TEN. Particularly rousing is Alicia's later battle with melanoma which had spread to her lungs and was successfully treated with immune checkpoint inhibitors (but not without further immune related adverse drug events (aseptic meningitis)).

II.

SJS/TEN is a "random attack" by one's own immune system that typically in adults occurs within a few days to a month after a new drug is introduced. It is characterized by detachment of the most superficial compartment of the skin – the epidermis- which can be mild (<10% skin body surface area detached (BSA), SJS) or severe (>30% skin BSA detached, TEN). Even when superficially less severe as measured by the percentage of skin that detaches other mucosal surfaces throughout the body are typically involved such as the eye, mouth, respiratory, gastrointestinal and genitourinary tracts. Long-term complications can be severe regardless of the BSA percentage of skin detached and can include blindness. In the acute stage of the disease the overwhelming concern and priority is to provide aggressive supportive care in an intensive care setting to promote early healing that leads to better survival, prevention of infection, and lower long-term complications. Although mortality currently averages 15% overall, with TEN, particularly in elderly patients with compromised immune systems, the mortality can be 50% or higher.

III.

SJS/TEN research has provided a glimmer of hope for prevention, prediction, early diagnosis and more effective treatments. Most notably this has included the discovery that specific human leukocyte antigen (HLA) genes are strongly associated with drug- induced SJS/TEN. In some countries such as Taiwan, Singapore and Hong Kong where these drug-gene associations are prevalent (e.g. HLA-B*15:02 and carbamazepine SJS/TEN) this has led to a genetic test being performed routinely prior to the prescription of carbamazepine with notable reduction in carbamazepine SJS/TEN. To optimize preventive efforts we need to urgently understand more about the risk genes that are important across populations of varied ethnicities across a broader range of drugs that are associated with SJS/TEN. This includes antibiotic for the treatment of common bacterial infections and tuberculosis, drugs used to treat and prevent seizures and mood disorders and allopurinol, a drug used to treat gout. Allopurinol, is a good example of a drug where in European and African ancestry individuals only 50-60% carry the HLA-B*58:01 risk allele that explains close to 100% of allopurinol SJS/TEN in South and East Asians. Aside from genetic markers to prevent SJS/TEN, research will also be important to help us understand measurable biological markers (e.g. granulysin) that will lead to earlier diagnosis of SJS/TEN. Studies that define the specific immune mechanisms that lead to SJS/TEN are ongoing and entail collecting a broad range of samples from the blister fluid and skin and studying individual cells and their specific signatures at the site of SJS/TEN disease. Understanding these mechanisms will be paramount to defining the most effective and targeted treatment approaches for SJS/TEN to lead to better short and long-term outcomes.

In 2017 and 2019 we have held NIH and FDA sponsored meetings to bring together a network of SJS/TEN researchers, survivors and family members to fuel efforts for research, support and awareness of this disease. (https://medsites.mc.vanderbilt.edu/sjsmeeting/welcome).(1 -3)

Below is a list of foundations and support groups within the United States and internationally available for SJS/TEN survivors and their families that provide links to resources and information about SJS/TEN. These groups also provide links to ongoing research studies on their websites and social media pages.

SJS Foundation http://sjsupport.org/ and registry http://sjsupport.org/?page_id=512
SJ Syndrome of Texas https://www.sjsyndrome.com/
SJS Awareness Oregon
https://www.sjsawarenessoregon.org/
Stevens Johnson Syndrome Canada
(http://www.sjscanada.org)
Amalyste (France; http://www.amalyste.fr/);
Awareness UK (United Kingdom;
https://www.sjsawareness.org.uk)

Elizabeth J Phillips, MD,
Professor of Medicine and Pharmacology
Professor of Pathology, Microbiology and Immunology
John A. Oates Chair in Clinical Research
Vanderbilt University Medical Center
drugsafetyresearch@vumc.org

IV.

1. White KD, Abe R, Ardern-Jones M, Beachkofsky T, Bouchard C, Carleton B, et al. SJS/TEN 2017: Building Multidisciplinary Networks to Drive Science and Translation. J Allergy Clin Immunol Pract. 2018;6(1):38-69.
2. Saeed HN, Bouchard C, Shieh C, Phillips E, Chodosh J. Highlights from the 2nd Biennial Stevens Johnson syndrome symposium 2019: SJS/TEN from Science to Translation. Ocul Surf. 2019.
3. Chang W, Abe R, Anderson P, Anderson W, Ardren-Jones M, Beachkofsky T et al . SJS/TEN 2019: From Science to Translation Journal of Dermatological Science. 2020 (accepted).

Made in the USA
Middletown, DE
03 March 2020